OUR NHS

David Owen

A Pan Original
Pan Books London, Sydney and Auckland

First published 1988 by Pan Books Ltd,
Cavaye Place, London SW10 9PG
9 8 7 6 5 4 3 2 1
© David Owen 1988
Hardback ISBN 0 330 30713 4
Paperback ISBN 0 330 30607 3
Photoset by Parker Typesetting Service, Leicester
Printed by Richard Clay Ltd, Bungay, Suffolk

This book is dedicated to
St Thomas' Hospital
and
The Hospital for Sick Children,
Great Ormond Street

Contents

Preface   1

Chapter 1
Our NHS   3

Chapter 2
The Medical Profession   13

Chapter 3
The Nursing Profession   31

Chapter 4
The Creation, Structure and Evolution of the NHS   44

Chapter 5
Lessons from Abroad   74

Chapter 6
A Market in Health   92

Chapter 7
Waiting Lists   109

Chapter 8
Community Care   119

Chapter 9
Public Health   135

Chapter 10
Paying for the NHS   157

References   183
Index   187

Preface

I was ten years old when the National Health Service first came into existence. My father, as a family doctor in the West Country, in Plymouth, was one of the minority of general practitioners who voted in the 1948 BMA referendum for the NHS. My mother was a dentist in the school dental service. My sister was a nurse and is a psychiatric social worker. Even now, I can recall the enthusiasm which existed in our home on the day when the NHS started. My father, not a very political person, had voted Labour for the first and only time in his life in 1945 because he wanted, as part of the post-war reconstruction, to see an end to the inadequate health care that he had practised before the war first hand in the mining villages of South Wales.

The day the NHS came into existence was the day my father gave up all his private patients, except for a few gypsies who never felt that they were getting proper treatment unless they paid in cash. The spirit of those doctors committed to the NHS was well expressed in an editorial in the well-respected medical journal, *Lancet*, at the time, seeing it as removing 'from medical practice much of the mercenary element that has been growing more conspicuous for fifty years or more. The new arrangements confer a great benefit on medicine by lessening the commercial element in its practice. Now that everyone is entitled to full medical care, the doctor can provide that care without thinking of his own profit or the patient's loss and can allocate his efforts more according to medical priority.'

That emphasis on medical priority is the best feature of the NHS. I have seen and welcomed its practical application as a medical student, neurological and psychiatric registrar, as a research fellow into the chemistry of the brain, as an MP in the constituency, as a father of three children, and as Minister of Health. My eldest son had childhood leukaemia and has been under continuous and, fortunately, successful treatment at the

1

Hospital for Sick Children in Great Ormond Street, London. At no time during the course of treatment, which costs something like £47 000, did we ever have any financial anxiety to add to all the other anxieties that we and many more families undergo in these circumstances. To say that the NHS was a blessing is to understate what it has given my family. My experience as a provider and a consumer of the NHS has, I hope, not made me blind to its defects. It has made me determined to defend the strengths of the NHS and resist those who wish to put at risk its future and introduce a two-tier health service, one public, the other private.

Chapter 1

OUR NHS

All professions are a conspiracy against the laity.

George Bernard Shaw, *The Doctor's Dilemma*

The National Health Service belongs to us all because it is personal to us all. Most of us have cause to be grateful to it at some time or other in our lives. A distinctive feature of the British health care system is the extensive range and personal nature of the care available. Our concept of the family doctor is unique. While it is not totally comprehensive, the coverage of the NHS, whether in hospital or at home, is nevertheless immense. There are no essential services which are not available free at the point of demand.

Yet far from celebrating its fortieth birthday on 5 July 1988, the NHS faces a greater challenge to its fundamental basis than at any time in its history. It is up to those of us who support the ethical principles on which the NHS is founded to come to its defence. The ethical foundations of the NHS must not be eroded or defaced as part of the transient movement and small change of party politics. They are timeless and well worth upholding.

The public debate about the future of the NHS is at present failing to show a fair balance between the achievements of the NHS and its deficiencies. It has also been naïve in the extreme, with simplistic solutions easily espoused without any attempt to understand the complexities and interrelationships. The frontline of the NHS is made up of the primary health care services which include all those provided outside hospital by family doctors, dentists, pharmacists and opticians, community

3

nursing staff and the professions allied to medicine. These services deal with over nine tenths of the contacts that the public have with the National Health Service. Yet this part of the NHS is rarely reported in the newspapers or featured on television. Newspaper headlines come from the delayed operations or the closure of whole hospitals or wards. The local hospital is often an emotional issue for those living in the neighbourhood. But sometimes closures are very necessary, particularly when they are no more than the inevitable consequence of the opening of a new hospital. Hospital or even ward closures can be justified as a way of concentrating resources and improving efficiency through increased turnover, for example, by increasing day surgery. What is impossible to defend is a brand new Health Service facility unable to open because of an unplanned shortage of funds. That rightly causes headlines and justified criticism. There has for decades been chronic under-funding of the NHS. In recent years, this has been cushioned in parts by efficiency savings. Yet these are becoming harder to achieve and the pinch is being felt in more and more health districts. We have short-term initiatives launched more with an eye to publicity than to effectiveness, one of the more ludicrous being when the government injected £25 million from the Department of Health and Social Security (DHSS) to reduce waiting lists in 1987. Yet at the same time, over 3000 beds were closed locally, thus increasing waiting lists, because of financial constraints on the district health authorities' normal budgets.

It is this feeling that in the DHSS, the right hand does not know what the left hand is doing, which is causing such exasperation within the NHS itself. Yet the public's sense of crisis in the NHS has been generated almost totally by failures in the acute services. Even these failures, though real enough, have on occasions been exaggerated by a few consultants or union leaders who have a vested interest in using a particular incident to generate public demand for more money or more resources. What is needed in proposing necessary reforms for the NHS is a sense of proportion. We are in danger of allowing a perception of crisis to become a self-fulfilling prophecy.

Problems the NHS certainly has, but there is no great mystery about the prime reason for these problems. We in the UK spend far less on health care than any other comparable western in-dustrialized nation. We are seventeenth in a league table of twenty-one OECD (Organization for Economic cooperation and Development) countries. When UK health care expenditure as a proportion of our gross domestic product (GDP) is compared to other western industrialized countries, the UK spends less than any other country with the exception of Greece, Spain, Portugal and New Zealand.

Table 1: **Total health expenditure as percentage of GDP, 1984**

Country	% of GDP	Country	% of GDP
1 United States	10.7	12 Finland	6.6
2 Sweden	9.4	13 Japan	6.6
3 France	9.1	14 Denmark	6.3
4 Netherlands	8.6	15 Norway	6.3
5 Canada	8.4	16 Belgium	6.2
6 Germany	8.1	17 United Kingdom	5.9
7 Ireland	8.0	18 Spain	5.8
8 Iceland	7.9	19 New Zealand	5.6
9 Australia	7.8	20 Portugal	5.5
10 Austria	7.2	21 Greece	4.6
11 Italy	7.2		

Source: *Measuring Health Care* 1960–83, OECD, Paris, 1985

As politicians trade statistics, it is easy to sow confusion. Though it is correct to say that UK expenditure has been rising steadily as a percentage of GDP, in 1949 £433 million was spent on the NHS. In 1988/9, it will be £23.5 billion, or four times as much in constant prices. It is misleading, however, not to add that as our NHS spending has increased, so has the health spending of other comparable countries.

The essential fact is that at 5.9% of GDP, not significantly changed since 1984, the UK's spending on health is considerably below the OECD average of 7.5%. Comparative studies also show per capita spending in the UK on total health care is nearly 30% below the level that would be expected in terms of the UK's

GDP per head. This relative constraint on our health spending has developed under Labour as well as Conservative governments over the last two decades. Labour's record on health spending is, in fact, marginally worse than that of the Conservatives, because during Labour's periods of office, the economy has not grown as fast. Who would have thought this would have occurred twenty years ago. Then Britain was spending 4% of national income on health, and the Americans little more than 5%, now those percentages damagingly have reached 6% and over 11% respectively. But it is worth pointing out that the US spends eight times as much private money on health and, without damaging the moral principles of the NHS, to increase private funds for health care in the UK is one obvious source of extra money. The truth is that the NHS has for decades given us all a relatively good service on the cheap.

International comparisons are always difficult, but the scale of the difference between what we spend as a percentage of our national wealth compared to others is so substantial that there can be no doubt that we must have a step-like increase in spending on the NHS over the next few years, particularly, since the relative price effect hits the Health Service hard. The reason is that NHS productivity savings are below average, so increases over the national inflation rate for the NHS still mean a reduction in financial support.

Is there a way of mobilizing the political will to produce such a step-like change? Arguing over whether there have been marginal increases or marginal decreases in NHS spending, as is done in the House of Commons, simply baffles the public. It does nothing to ease their concern. In the 1988 budget, the resources were there for an increased investment in the NHS, but the government refused to act. It preferred to wait until April to announce an injection of extra money to finance the nurses' pay award. The Kings Fund estimated that in addition to the nurses' increase, £400 million extra spending in 1988/9 would make up for the past six years' shortfall and allow the NHS to start from a new base. Even such a new base would not be sufficient. The SDP suggested that to help fill the gap the Chancellor should change Premium Bonds into health bonds to provide a new and imaginative source of extra private money. Health bonds would allow people both to save for themselves and save the NHS. The present yearly payment of just under £100 million from National Savings Premium Bonds to the Exchequer would become an NHS innovation fund. With TV advertising it could rise to £250 million or more, private money.

The best hope until 1992 for a new approach and greater generosity towards the NHS is from the fundamental review started in 1988 and controlled directly by the Prime Minister. The government has hitherto not accepted that the NHS has been under-funded. It also, with some justification, fears to drip-feed the NHS. This government is more likely to shift towards more generous funding of the NHS if it is done in a wider context of reform and with some guarantee that extra money will ensure tangible improvements in standards of patient care. All experience indicates, and the case is argued in Chapter 10, Paying for the NHS, that we will not see a step-like increase in the NHS budget without there first being a decision to make specific changes in the way we finance the NHS. In theory, a step-like increase in the NHS budget could be achieved within the present system. It is, however, very unlikely. Of all the suggested new systems of funding, a hypothecated health tax, levied like income tax, and creating an autonomous health fund, is the best. This is a mechanism whereby the public will be able to translate their repeatedly expressed willingness to spend more on the NHS into reality. Such a specific health tax breaches none of the fundamental principles on which the NHS was founded. It could provide the basis for a cross-party agreement lasting well into the next forty years of the NHS.

Yet this government could decide from its review that there is no case for a step-like increase in NHS funds, in which case the other positive reforms suggested in this book will be even more necessary – the most innovative of which are: ensuring that the professions study health economics and practise medical audit and resource management; linking the hospital and family practitioner services formally together; a statutory right to enable patients who are waiting too long for treatment to have treatment in another district or in a private hospital; the creation of an internal market between district health authorities; a carer's charter and a voucher system with a variable carer's allowance;

and the move towards health maintenance attitudes and preventive medicine.

Even if the government were to decide – wrongly – that the NHS had to continue with much the same projected levels of funding, it will still have to provide an improved service. The raw Health Service statistics fortunately show a formidable record of activity and achievement, giving grounds for hope rather than despair. On an average working day in England, about two thirds of a million people consult their family doctor, about 270 000 go to the dentist, and more than 75 000 are visited by nurses or other health professionals working in the community. Each year, more and more patients are treated. Those who are treated in hospitals as inpatients stay for less time, which allows more patients to be treated per bed. In 1986–7, there was a 9% increase in the number of day cases, which has made it possible for patients who formerly had to spend several days in hospital to return home the same day.

Medical technology has made staggering progress. Ten years ago, only two in ten babies born weighing less than 1000g survived the critical first month of life. Now, five in ten survive. The proportion of very low weight babies born alive has increased by 33% in the last five years, and these very small babies make up about 1% of all births. Nevertheless, they need long-term intensive care facilities and this requires highly skilled paediatric nurses. We are now finding that instead of a shortage of money or insufficient operating theatres, it is a shortage of skilled nurses that is delaying children's heart operations, and meaning that severely ill babies are having to be transferred to intensive care units miles from their mothers' homes. Nurse recruitment and retention have become crucial as fewer eighteen-year-old women come on to the job market and become nurses.

Virtually all new babies and their parents are seen in their homes in the first year of life by a health visitor, and over 80% of these babies also attend health clinics. Over 70% of all children between the ages of one and five were seen by health visitors, and over three quarters of children between four and fourteen were seen in school by nurses as part of child health surveillance programmes. In line with the increasing number of people living beyond the age of seventy-five, there has been the expected increase in the number of inpatient cases treated in geriatric departments – a 3.7% increase in 1985–6 and an 8.1% increase in the number of outpatient attendances. There was a matching 8.1% increase in the number of consultant geriatricians and a 1.2% increase in the number of wholetime equivalent doctors working in geriatric departments.

Against such a background, serious though the problems are, talk of a collapse of the NHS itself is an exaggeration. It will not collapse, if for no other reason than that within the NHS there are thousands of people who will go on working in substandard conditions, for far longer hours than they are paid for, because they are dedicated to sustain it. Those who wish the NHS well, politicians as well as physicians, nurses as well as surgeons, trade unionists as well as managers, must avoid deepening the public's anxiety over the NHS and generating out of their own sense of despair the self-destructive pursuit of alternatives to the NHS which have no greater intrinsic merit and many disadvantages.

The NHS has been grossly under-funded in terms of capital growth and badly managed for many years. Those are correctable problems. It undoubtedly needs steady administrative reform, and also a steady increase in capital to ensure its continued success. The status quo may suit vested interests, but it does not carry much conviction. The NHS is no longer, if it ever was, the envy of the world. Yet many features within it are admired around the world. Its ethical basis is, quite simply, right, and to destroy that would be a wanton act of political vandalism. It is time for those of us who have lived our lives predominantly within the era of the NHS to assert why its continued existence matters to us. We must state clearly why the NHS, of all the institutions in our country, still commands the respect and earns the admiration of the vast majority of us. It is very much *our* NHS.

It can only stay that way if the consumer's rights are protected and indeed enlarged. One cannot escape the conclusion that the NHS is too orientated towards, and dominated by, the providers. The professions of medicine and nursing grow stronger while patient powers dwindle. The community health councils seem to have less influence. The existing inspectorates appear to have become institutionalized, taken over by bureaucratic attitudes and too respectful of the vested interests of the professions. The

Health Commissioner or ombudsman is suffocatingly constrained. Patients must now be given rights. That becomes easier within a more market-orientated NHS than within a collectivist NHS. The laity, in George Bernard Shaw's famous dictum, are the ones for whom the NHS is designed, not the professions.

The reality of becoming a patient often changes people's attitudes to the NHS, sometimes for good but, it has to be admitted, sometimes for ill. For every satisfied customer, fortunately still the majority, there are too many who emerge feeling they are a mere statistic – an inanimate object, being 'put through' the system. Too often, they meet an attitude from the providers that comes across to them as 'it's all free, you are lucky to get it'. There have to be countervailing pressures to ensure that because a patient does not pay at the point of the delivery of health care, they should be treated no differently from someone who is either writing a cheque or whose insurance company is writing a cheque. There is no excuse for a difference of attitude to be shown towards the patient in the public sector from that shown to one who goes privately.

Sadly, the economic stringency of many years, the frustrations and sheer tiredness, often blunt the caring edge of NHS staff; the emphasis on numbers treated, through-put, have all contributed to this. While it is important that we are seeing the publication in 1988 of 'performance indicators', there are dangers that this approach is becoming all-pervasive. The vision of mutual respect and care in 1948 is being eroded. There are many ways in which this tendency can be checked and even corrected. Hitherto perhaps there has been too much stress on participation in the management of the Health Service by the lay person, when what is really important is that those who manage the NHS should take on board the new mood of consumerism. This means better communication and personal participation by all staff with the patient.

The shop whose staff never smile, who never address a word to their customers, soon loses business to the shop around the corner. The NHS may not lose business, but it can lose support. In 1983, the Annual British Social Attitudes Series asked, 'How satisfied are you with the way in which the NHS runs nowadays?' Then, 55% were satisfied and only 25% dissatisfied. Since then, there has been a gradual increase in the numbers dissatisfied, but in 1988, for probably the first time in the NHS's history, a majority were expressing dissatisfaction with the service. Only 37% were satisfied and 46% registered their dissatisfaction. These are very damaging figures, particularly when one notes that whereas only 7% were *very* dissatisfied in 1983, 11% in 1984, 16% in 1986, by 1988 25% were *very* dissatisfied. These consumer concerns should be in the front of the mind of everyone who is looking at reform of the National Health Service.

The popularity of some private health schemes does not just stem from the fact that they allow somebody to avoid an NHS waiting list, but that they make their customers feel at home and cosseted at a time when they need it most. The NHS has not developed the consumer commitment it ought to have done. In the health context, the 'consumer' will never have enough information to make well-informed judgements, but in relations with their general practitioner, as far as possible there should be some joint decision-making about which hospital and which consultant patients would like to go to. The patient should not feel that referral to another doctor is something over which they have no influence at all. In this context, the new emphasis on quality of service is greatly to be welcomed. It does not of itself give the patient more power but it does give the patient a feeling that they are obtaining a good service, and that there is some rationale behind their GP's judgement as to where they should go. Quality assurance is an essential part of the new general management philosophy introduced into the Health Service by the First Griffiths Report in 1984, and the best general manager will see this as a further lever for raising the profile of the patient against the sometimes overwhelming professionalism of the staff.

We need to define, in terms of the utmost clarity, the respective roles of the local authorities and the health authorities concerning the long-term responsibility for the care and welfare of the elderly, the mentally ill and mentally handicapped. It is noteworthy that the nomenclature changes: hospitals have 'patients'; social services departments have 'clients'; but both, all too often, have games of 'pass the responsibility' as the patient or client fails to be seen as the total responsibility of one or the other. Occasionally, people of vision and determination manage to make some sense in this disputed area, and the arrangements for the planned run-down of the psychiatric hospitals and hospitals for the mentally handicapped, while not perfect, have in some cases shown a considerable degree of cooperation across the authorities. The concept of partnership can therefore be made to work.

General managers are not just there to sharpen the leadership of the local health service, but they should also see their role as defender of the patient's interests. There are other contenders as to who cares for the patient's interests. There is no need for competition or confusion. The health care professionals, the doctors and nurses, claim with some justification that this is their hallowed tradition. But not only do they sometimes fail to live up to this tradition, they often resent the intrusion of the manager, not realizing that together they can often provide a far more effective service for the patient. The other contenders are the local community health councils, which often wish to see themselves as the 'patient's friend', and also the members of the DHA who not infrequently resent the role and presence of a community health council. Yet all these elements have a contribution to make as long as they recognize that 'patients first' is not just a slogan but the reason for the very existence of the National Health Service.

Chapter 2

THE MEDICAL PROFESSION

From inability to let well alone, from too much zeal
for the new and contempt for what is old, from
putting knowledge before wisdom, science before art
and cleverness before common sense, from treating
patients as cases and for making the cure of the
disease more grievous than the endurance of the
same, good Lord deliver us.

Sir Robert Hutchison, *The Physician's Prayer*

Who shall decide when doctors disagree?

Alexander Pope

To understand the NHS one has first to comprehend the nature
and influence of the medical profession. The powerful medical
profession that we know in Britain today was only just coming
into existence 150 years ago. Fragmented – neither very well
regarded nor rewarded – it would have been hard then to have
predicted its emergence as one of the most powerful influences
on modern society. The social history of medicine in the nineteenth century shows a transformation dominated by the tension
that developed between the extension of the market in medical
care and its restriction. In medicine, as in all walks of life, the
principles of economic liberalism vied with the forces of social
protectionism. As the demand for medical care increased, the
individual medical practitioner became less dependent on the
patronage of a few wealthy patients. Whereas in the eighteenth
century the patient was the dominant figure in the relationship

with the doctor, by the middle of the nineteenth century their roles were reversed.

Physicians, surgeons and the despised apothecaries gradually became identified simply as general medical practitioners. In 1858, Parliament created a single register for all practitioners and a council to coordinate all medical education in the United Kingdom. The growth in the power and the influence of the medical profession in the English-speaking world has been spectacular ever since, first starting in Britain, then gathering pace and well surpassing Britain in the United States. Why is this so? It was not an inevitable trend. In the Roman Empire, the physician was an inferior member of society. In the eighteenth century, surgeons were barbers who switched to operating having, one hoped, refined their shaving and hair-cutting techniques. In 1869, it was possible to write in an article on American versus European medical science, 'In all our American colleges, medicine has ever been and is now, the most despised of all the professions which liberally educated men are expected to enter.'[1]

The healers have not always been given status and esteem. In the Soviet Union, over many years, the medical practitioner has been positioned low in the hierarchy of science. Even today, in part because of the large number of women practitioners in Russia, average pay is low, although many find ways of supplementing their income. Probably the less deferential style of a Soviet society makes it easier to regard medical practitioners as only one of many trained resources, less valuable to society than engineers or scientists. In the western democracies, where private citizens' values and liberties are precious, we have been more ready to give medical practitioners deference and respect as people who bridge the personal, private and subjective world of the individual with the scientific, public and objective world of science.

The social transformation of the medical profession has been quite dramatic and is best exemplified in America, where 'in the nineteenth century the medical profession was generally weak, divided, insecure in its status and its income, unable to control entry into practice or to raise the standards of medical education. In the twentieth century, not only did physicians become

powerful, prestigious and wealthy professionals but they suc-
ceeded in shaping the basic organization and financial structure
of American medicine.'[2]

The motor for this transformation, on both sides of the
Atlantic, has been twofold: the medical profession's insistence
that its members should be independent contractors, not salaried
servants; and that they should sell their services to patients, not to
organizations. In a sense, the medical profession attempted to
reverse the historical trend. Just at the moment when small
shopkeepers and manufacturers were starting to be absorbed
into larger units, when the economies of scale were the dominating influence within industrialized democracies, the medical
profession set out to establish its independence. This was based
on a compelling mixture of ethical and moral principles allied to
the values, but not the financial disciplines, of small-scale capital-
ism. The profession stressed the critical role of clinical freedom,
the right to make an unfettered judgement about what doctors as
professionals felt was in the best interest of an individual patient.
The vital importance of confidentiality was highlighted to
emphasize the one-to-one doctor/patient relationship. Public
opinion was receptive to the profession's argument and politicians had to take account of this public support. Medicine was
making new advances and discoveries, and the public wanted
reassurance; they wanted to believe in the infallibility of the
profession. The profession was able, therefore, to establish its
independence and autonomy and to free itself of the encroach-
ment of monopoly power and bureaucracy so evident elsewhere
in society, because it was able to persuade the public that medicine
could be isolated from economic pressures. Medicine could, in
effect, grow and prosper without the economic constraints
imposed by market pressures or public expenditure limits.

The early part of the twentieth century was a golden age for
the medical profession in Britain in every sense. The profession
was both well regarded and well rewarded and its standing was
exceptionally high. The medical profession, through organization and effective lobbying, had by then shaped the medical
system itself, so that education, payment and conditions of service buttressed its professional sovereignty instead of under-
mining it. That sovereignty was perhaps at its peak in the UK in

the 1930s, though it was not to reach its peak in the United States until some decades later. Yet even by then, the basis of that professional sovereignty was being undermined, for it was founded on a myth – that clinical freedom and economic freedom were synonymous.

It was, in retrospect at least, obvious that the medical profession would not be able, throughout the twentieth century, to isolate itself from the political and economic constraints with which other professionals, whether in the armed services or education, all had to contend. The pressure started in 1883 when Germany introduced the first national system of compulsory sickness insurance followed by similar schemes in Austria and Hungary. In 1911 in Britain, the national insurance scheme was started. By the 1930s, that scheme's flaws created the climate for a further move towards a comprehensive and universal health care system. So enthusiastic became the advocates for the NHS that by the time of its introduction, the conventional wisdom in the UK was that, after a period of initially higher expenditure, there would then be a fall in expenditure as the nation's health improved. That was naïve nonsense as we now know, but at the time – at the dawn of the antibiotic era – not quite as foolish as it now appears.

Britain was the first western democracy to find, after the end of the Second World War, the political authority – against a background of centralized wartime controls – to challenge the medical profession and impose state control, in the face of opposition from its organized voice, the British Medical Association (BMA). This unleashed a polemical debate about the dangers of socialized medicine to the doctor's independence. Forty years on, it is not state control that is the major force curbing the independence of doctors. The spiralling health care costs in the US have identified the critical force challenging the hitherto inviolate authority of the American medical profession as the corporate private insurance sector. In the United States, this pressure is far more powerful than that which is coming from government through the administration of Medicare and Medicaid. In Britain, government control is far more overt, but nowhere near as strong as some of the US corporate controls. Yet in all countries, it is basic economic forces that are challenging professional autonomy.

Whatever a country spends as a percentage of its GDP on health, the pressures exist to increase that percentage, and these pressures, whether demographic, technological or professionally inspired, are similar in kind. Against such an international background, the wiser heads in the medical profession know that it is no longer credible for them to continue to assume that they can opt out of the economic choices inherent in any health system.

The fact is that under different health care systems, whether privately or publicly provided, the members of the medical profession are now demonstrably making major economic decisions.

It is unrealistic for the medical profession to try to claim that its members are only making clinical decisions. The choices that they make in the short term may appear to be made in purely clinical circumstances; but the economic effects of such decisions, they increasingly realize, have profound consequences for their future choices in relation to patients and treatments. To take the example of a common surgical operation like an appendectomy, one study, for instance, has shown that by lowering the symptom threshold for undertaking an appendicitis operation enough to save one life, it would be necessary to perform so many operations on normal patients that there would not only be a huge cost but a loss of 2053 person-years in convalescence.[3]

Doctors tend to argue that it is not for them to lower or raise the administrative or financial criteria for conducting operations, that they must act at all times only in the best interests of that particular patient. Economic criteria for conducting operations are, many doctors would say, political questions. But this is changing. In 1980, the General Medical Council said of basic medical education, 'the necessary understanding of medicine as an evolving discipline must be attacked through the study of the physical, biological, behavioural and social sciences and by the study of man himself in health and disease.' By including social sciences, there was the implication that health economics was legitimate and when discussing the teaching of community medicine, 'simple health care economics' was to be included. But a survey of medical schools in 1985 showed that, of the twenty-five schools studied, six had no undergraduate programme in health economics. Three quarters of those which did have a programme devoted four hours or less to the subject. Nine schools, however, said they planned to increase time devoted to the subject of health economics. But there is little doubt that most doctors by the twenty-first century will have to include economic factors as a matter of course in any clinical judgement.

There have been many economic studies assessing the screening of breast cancer, cancer of the cervix and foetal screening, and assessing the costs and benefits of day care versus inpatient care and home care versus hospital care. With life-expectancy measurement and the cost-benefit of survival also came an emphasis on the quality of life. The attempt has been made to link longevity and a person's wellbeing into units of 'quality adjusted life years' (QALYs). The concept of quality of life measurements threatens those doctors who prefer to go on doing things without questioning the consequences of their actions. The urge to intervene, to act, even when all one is doing is propping up an ageing structure, is very strong. 'Can't you do something, doctor?' is an age-old cry to which the pharma-ceutical industry has geared itself to encourage the doctor to respond.

A political lead is needed to help point a way forward through the moral dilemmas associated with health economics and the rationing of care. Yet in the end, it will be far better if it is the doctor who balances what a particular patient and their symp-toms need with what they know to be the likely consequences for that patient, and in terms of resources for other areas of care as well.

A study in Canada in 1968, before the Canadian system of health finance was changed, and when doctors were paid for every operation, found that the rates of surgical intervention were 1.8 times higher for men and 1.6 times higher for women in Canada than in England and Wales. Yet mortality rates were no higher.[4] Not surprisingly, item-by-service payments for sur-gery generate a greater tendency to operate. A paradox is that many of the same doctors who argue trenchantly against a rationing system based on health need in the NHS are more than happy to participate in a rationing process, based overtly on the capacity to pay, in their part-time private practice.

The Royal Colleges are, however, very encouragingly giving the lead to the profession. Each has introduced a requirement for medical audit where consultants seek accreditation for training young doctors in their speciality. The General Medical Council is looking at recertification where doctors might, from time to time, have to demonstrate they are up to date. They are making it clear too that clinical freedom cannot be a licence to ignore all considerations of cost and resources in the practice of clinical medicine and surgery. Yet while the medical student remains insulated from a systematic education in the implications of these critical economic factors for a doctor's clinical freedom, changes in attitude will take much longer to achieve.

All the evidence there is suggests that, if medical need is not infinite in its technological applications, it is certainly so large relative to the resources that society is able to provide now and in the foreseeable future that no health care system can ever hope to meet it completely. When health care systems adapt to meet demands they find demand expands to meet supply. In the NHS, a substantial study of 177 large acute hospitals found that both admissions and length of stay increased with bed availability. In fact, no level of bed provision could be found which would have fully satisfied doctors' demands to meet the needs of their patients.

In a zero-price market such as dominates the British NHS, no financial discipline exists to curb excess demand unless a sophisticated self-discipline is developed among medical decision-makers to ensure that financial considerations are always taken into account. That is why many who strongly believe in a health service based on medical need are quite convinced that it is vital that doctors become more aware of financial consideration and support wholeheartedly the concept of the medical audit. In this way, the medical practitioner within the NHS would not entirely escape the disciplines of cost-effectiveness associated with market medicine, even when practising within the structure of public medicine. That is why bringing the discipline of an internal market into the NHS is a far more important reform than changing direction towards a private-insurance-based health care system with all its known failings. Changes in medical attitude towards the cost of health care are now far more important than further structural changes. There are too many doctors who ignore the cost implications of health care, whether they practise in private or NHS hospitals.

Doctors in all health care systems have to decide which patients to spend most of their time on; what drugs to prescribe; what treatment courses to pursue; the place of treatment and length of stay. Implicit within each decision is the choice to use available resources in one way rather than another. Hospitalizing a patient, for example, usually automatically means that somebody else is excluded from that particular hospital bed. Hospitalization is also often more expensive than keeping a patient in their own home and arranging for community nursing staff to visit, for meals-on-wheels to be delivered, and the home help service to come.

Doctors have, perhaps understandably, not tended to think of themselves as economic decision-makers. But in part as a consequence, they have been agents for limiting the provision of health care. This has taken place implicitly when resource constraints have made themselves felt in the form of queues, waiting lists, or shortage of time of available medical personnel. One result of doctors distancing themselves from the economics of health care is that it has been easier for them to concentrate on deficiencies and criticize an overall shortage of resources rather than to examine critically their own deployment of resources and the cost-effectiveness of health care.

Both as a doctor and as a politician, I recognize that clinical freedom is a very precious concept, and one which I have long argued the medical profession is right to cherish.[5] If politicians or administrators start to make economic choices without involving doctors, doctors will face a genuine curtailment of clinical freedom. The maintenance of clinical freedom necessitates the involvement of doctors in the process of choice and in the ordering of priorities. Since financial and other resources are not limitless, and since medical need is in effect limitless, someone somewhere has to choose. That person should be the doctor.

It is right for doctors to demand that politicians should openly acknowledge the limitations within which medical practice has to operate. It is also fair to say that, in the past, politicians have not sought openly and frankly to explain these limitations to the public. Yet clinical freedom is not an abstract concept. Its full realization demands that the medical profession face the practical economic facts of life. The constraint on the total resources available means that doctors acting individually can constrain the clinical freedom of their colleagues and also limit the effectiveness of health care for other patients. One interpretation of clinical freedom is that there is no need for an individual doctor to worry about any of this, that they simply have to demand the best for all their patients and sit back and let the politicians and the voters between them sort out where the money is to come from. George Bernard Shaw wrote: 'Freedom incurs responsibility, that is why so many men fear it.' Clinical freedom likewise means responsibility, that is why so many doctors are afraid of facing up to its true implications. The hard but true definition of clinical freedom includes the responsibility it carries for involvement in choosing priorities within the totality of health care.

Unbridled clinical freedom pre-empts scarce resources, whether skills or expenditure, and impacts on their availability for all patients, whether in a market or collective health care system. The freedom of one physician to practise as they see fit can easily come at the expense of another physician. The nature of the health care available to one patient can influence the quality and nature of the care available to another patient.

Government has now been joined by private insurers in demanding that high medical expenditure levels are constrained and that a fairer and more rational distribution of available health care is introduced. They are responding to the needs and wishes of voters and subscribers who can, of course, be one and the same person. For the medical profession, the implications of this new trend are profound, for the corporation is much more ruthless in the pursuit of economies and rationalization of services than government has ever been or is ever likely to be. The corporation can be lobbied only by shareholders interested in profits, not by voters interested in services. In the United States, where the medical profession has hitherto been able to claim a greater freedom than in the UK because of the absence of governmental control, there is a real prospect that before the end of this century its members will be envying the clinical freedom of their professional colleagues in Britain. It will be an odd reversal of roles if the American Medical Association, the bitter critic of socialized medicine, has to swallow far more clinical controls within the orbit of market medicine than ever the state would dare to impose on a vocal lobby like the British Medical Association.

The rise of the corporate ethos in medical care in the US has recently been described as permeating voluntary hospitals, government agencies and academic thought, as well as profit-making medical care organizations. 'Those who talked about "health care planning" in the 1970s now talk about "health care marketing". Everywhere one sees the growth of a kind of marketing mentality in health care . . . The organizational culture of medicine used to be dominated by the ideals of professionalism and voluntarism, which softened the underlying acquisitive activity. The restraint exercised by those ideals now grows weaker. The "health centre" of one era is the "profit centre" of the next.'[2] The language of marketing has come in the 1980s to the NHS as well; the privatization debate has impacted on the health sector. Competitive tendering and the selling of services have influenced the language within the NHS and had some direct influence on the medical profession and even the health service unions. No one objects to selling off surplus NHS land and buildings. The presence of banks, florists and newsagents within hospitals has hitherto been on a very small scale; but few object now to extending these activities.

The interesting aspect of the market mentality in US medicine is how the medical profession is reacting against it or accommodating to it. Rationalizing medical care in the private sector is meaning more private regulation, albeit not public regulation, more corporate planning, albeit not public planning. The process of accommodation shows every sign of involving a considerable loss of professional autonomy. The federal government has had to be more involved in Medicaid and Medicare. The growth, though some predict this will now level off, of health maintenance organizations (HMOs) offering better value than the fee-for-service system is an interesting phenomenon. In the

US, private corporations and the federal and state governments are taking every opportunity to cut health care costs.

In Britain, a somewhat similar pattern is emerging as the government's 'enterprise culture' impacts on the public sector. The emphasis on the general manager, the discipline of cash limits, the introduction of an NHS Management Board, 'performance indicators' for health authorities, the process of annual review, resource-management initiatives for six acute hospitals, cost-improvement programmes, competitive tendering, cross-financing arrangements between the expanding private sector and income-generation proposals are all creating a more market-orientated attitude even within the NHS. The medical profession knows that it cannot insulate itself from these trends, even if it wanted to. Yet as the general practitioners tried to fight off the imposition of cash limits during the passage of the health legislation through the House of Commons in 1988, one sensed that old habits die hard; there is still a conviction that clinical demand must be fully met regardless of cost.

Hospital consultants are still nowhere near accountable enough. Output per consultant, complications per consultant, and commitment per consultant can vary as much as a hundredfold. In hospital practice, hesitantly but more and more frequently, consultants are using the techniques of medical audit. But the concept of a clinical team with an elected chairman and executive responsibility for the team's performance is still considered too intrusive.

The Review Body on Doctors' and Dentists' Remuneration in their eighteenth report in 1988[6] said that there may be a case for examining the concept of permanent-distinction and meritorious awards, renewable after review. They wanted to single out consultants who continue to give outstanding service to the NHS and also thought it desirable to involve management in the selection process. These are all trends towards greater accountability which should be followed up quickly and implemented.

The Confidential Enquiry into Maternal Deaths has, since 1952, examined every death in and around childbirth and has proved a powerful mechanism for helping steadily to reduce deaths in childbirth. In 1977, the Association of Anaesthetists started to review their cases to establish the degree to which anaesthetic had contributed to death. The problem was that when the results were made known in 1982, they produced headline stories purporting to show how incompetent anaesthetists were. Fortunately, the anaesthetists were not put off and, together with the surgeons, they started to study more than half a million operations over a year in three regions. Their report, the *Confidential Enquiry into Peri-operative Deaths*, was published in December 1987,[7] and on the day of publication, the Minister of Health wisely found an initial £250 000 followed by £500 000 a year for five years to set up a national system for auditing deaths after surgery in all fourteen English RHAs.

The study found that the overall death rate was only 0.7% – 4034 deaths. Most were, as one would expect, in patients aged over seventy-five where there was either advanced cancer or failure of the heart or lungs. Yet the authors found their results extremely disquieting in that 195 deaths were due to failure by surgeons, and three were the result of errors by anaesthetists, and if these figures were extrapolated to cover all NHS regions, there would be around 1000 avoidable deaths a year occurring as a result of surgery. Perhaps the most worrying aspect of the report was the finding that many operations were undertaken by surgeons too junior and too inexperienced to do the job, that they were making mistakes because of failures of supervision. There were also too many out-dated or inappropriate operations being performed by surgeons who did not have specialized expertise – general surgeons doing non-urgent brain surgery and orthopaedic surgeons undertaking bowel surgery. Nevertheless, resistance to such quality-control studies within the medical profession appears to be diminishing. In future, they should cover the private sector as well as the NHS, and that would provide an interesting comparison between consultant-led treatment in the private sector where the consultant operates on a patient, and consultant-based care in the NHS where the consultant heads a team but does not always operate.

Doctors in all countries are becoming ever more aware of the limitations of present medical care systems in terms of improved patient health. Nor can doctors ignore the fact that iatrogenic, doctor-induced, disease is so prevalent. One US study found that 9% of patients in receipt of general medical service had their lives threatened or severely disabled as a result of treatment.[8] In England, the estimated number of discharges, including deaths in hospitals of inpatients with the main diagnosis of post-operative infection, was 6890, and subsidiary diagnosis of post-operative infection was 8720. Those who had a main diagnosis of aplastic anaemia numbered 2820 in 1985.

It appears that, slowly, the weight of the US medical profession is coming behind those doctors who wish to change and redirect the content of the present technologically orientated medical care system, and to stress the role of the physician in the care of the whole patient. Changing that content means a radical shift away from a sickness service to a health service, away from the engineering approach to medicine towards the holistic approach, where the market element is balanced by the social element in medical care.

Despite the strong commercialization of United States medical care, there has been a discernible shift of attitude, first manifesting itself in a revival of interest in preventive health. It is symbolic that this shift has been magnified and accelerated in the US by the pressures of corporate medicine. In a sense, the very individualism of the past, a characteristic of the medical profession's assumed sovereignty, lends itself to supporting a decentralized philosophy of personal responsibility, self-determination, self-regulation, and social accountability. In the US, the medical profession, for so long opposed to state control, is being forced to support the structure of a market health care system that is starting to develop its own controls and to challenge the very medical profession that was its greatest champion.

The growth in many countries of malpractice cases and rising costs of insurance for the medical practitioner are all signs of a changed relationship developing between patient and physician. Patients as consumers, whether they pay directly or indirectly, are both more knowledgeable and more demanding. This is making the doctor/patient relationship less deferential. Patients are less likely to accept the automatic authority of the doctor over their case, and there is more interest in natural methods of treatment and prevention.

The good clinician has nothing to fear from self-reliance.

They understand that the body has an ability to heal itself, but that if they intervene to correct one factor, an imbalance will often appear somewhere else. The wise clinician never diagnoses or treats any symptom in isolation: the whole person embraces their environment just as much as their ailment. Doctors should know better than the general public that more medicine does not equal more health. A dramatic fall in the death rate during the nineteenth and twentieth centuries, when the reputation of the profession soared in the public mind, was not due to miracle medicines but to the improvements in hygiene and public health. The dramatic fall in deaths from tuberculosis, doctors know, preceded the discovery of the drugs that killed the tubercule. That knowledge tended to be reserved to the profession but it has now been extended to a wider audience. The medical killers we all now know are the degenerative diseases, associated with prosperity and progress. The life expectancy of adults in the US has not improved in the thirty-two years during which national expenditure on medical care has risen from $12 billion in 1950 to over $275 billion in 1987. Only 5% of that budget was devoted to health promotion with 95% devoted to disease care.

The question for the medical profession in Britain is this: should it continue to put its considerable weight behind the status quo, which is essentially a sickness service heavily orientated towards technological medicine? Or should it attempt a fundamental rethink and promote prevention of ill health? The 'rule of halves', as it is sometimes called, is a salutary reminder of how far we have to go. Half the diabetics are not known to the medical profession in Britain today; half of those with blood pressure sufficiently high to pose a threat to their health are not known, and only half of those known are being treated and only half of those are being adequately treated. Asthma and bronchitis are probably as unknown as diabetes.

A self-confident profession or, somewhat paradoxically, even one under attack, should respond to such facts by instituting a profound change in practice and in philosophy. I would like to believe that as the ideological pressures for reform of the NHS gather momentum, the medical profession in Britain will use its weight to defeat the zealotry of those who believe market medicine can solve all our problems. As natural scientists, the medical profession know well the value of evolution. British medicine has had a strong tradition of personal idealism and individualism. There is a long-acknowledged place for market-orientated competitive pressures and consumer choice. But there is also a wider, and indeed deeper, tradition. The history of science honours the role of holistic medicine where the concept of 'wholeness' means treating and caring for the whole person.

NHS reform should point away from a sickness service. The future of medicine lies, not in developing ever larger institutions filled with ever more costly medical technology, but in rediscovering old truths, and the values enshrined in public health. A sensible deployment of limited resources would redistribute money to give incentives to promote good health. The degree to which preventive care has been neglected in the rush towards interventionist and technological medicine is a scandal.

It would be of immense value if the medical profession itself were to foster public changes in attitude to prevention. This is starting to happen as the status and influence of general practice steadily increase. Instead of the hospital specialists being the driving force within the NHS, that role is being transferred to general practitioners. Over 50% of medical students now put general practice as their first choice of career. As able people come into general practice, they extend its role. The referral rate of new outpatients from general practice is now half what it was in the early 1960s. GPs are now referring only 155 patients for every 1000 on their list, compared to 320 then. GP pathology requests now amount to 25% of the total hospital workload and x-ray requests amount to 10%. As GPs do more active diagnosis and treatment, it not only reduces the demands on hospitals, but it generates in GPs a wider interest in the patients they treat. As they become responsible for the whole of their patients' treatment, so they tend to become more interested in the natural history of disease and look to prevention and the origins of illness. It costs £110 000 to train a family doctor.

To a considerable extent, a redistribution of resources away from hospitals is happening which has nothing to do with general practice but is coming from patients themselves. Medical self-care is part of the 'self-help', 'do-it-yourself' movement which has exploded across many different spheres. But it is a real question for the medical profession whether this movement must encounter medical indifference and, sometimes, hostility, or find a supportive enthusiastic atmosphere where self-help becomes not just an appendage of modern medicine, but an integral part. In a sense, this raises the whole relationship between the volunteer and the professional. The voluntary movement was, at one time, central to our medical care system in this country. It had been squeezed by the growth of public provision but is now, once again, finding itself in demand and generating enthusiasm. The growth of the hospice movement for the terminally ill is an example of what the voluntary movement can do. On a less sophisticated level, we are seeing a trend from do-it-yourself pregnancy testing to monitoring blood pressure, heartbeat and even taking smears. From the self-help mentality which led to the funding of Alcoholics Anonymous has grown a plethora of such groups, from Weight Watchers' groups to people who organize themselves around conditions of schizophrenia, to Alzheimer's disease and Well Women clinics.

If the self-help movement is to work with professional providers of medical care and if the voluntary movement is to work well with the public, then they need to be welcomed, not shunned; seen as an additional resource, not an additional burden. This will require a reorientation of medical attitudes, starting in medical schools. It will mean reassessing the role of the community in the development of patterns of medical care, particularly necessary given the demographic pressures of an ageing population with more living beyond the age of eighty and more people with severe handicaps living longer. It will mean the restoration of the supportive community. That means building an infrastructure where social concern can bear fruit and manifest itself in an urban environment as well as the more traditional, though often illusory, image of community care in a rural setting.

The traditional moral values of British medicine should be used as a counterweight: not to resist the mechanistic cost-effectiveness of the market place that will inevitably and rightly influence the NHS from across the Atlantic and Continental

Europe, but to keep those pressures in their proper context – improving patient care but not destroying a patient's individuality; retaining the one-to-one relationship implicit in family doctoring which remains one of the strongest parts of the NHS.

Such confidence in British medicine is vulnerable to the charge that it is the idealistic musing of a doctor turned politician who is trying to find ways of avoiding finding the financial resources that medicine needs in a modern age. I hope rather it is an assertion that the true values that have underpinned the profession of medicine in Britain make it natural for the profession to see the virtue of health promotion and disease prevention. These are now urgent priorities. Holistic medicine cannot replace technological and therapeutic medicine, but it is an all-important complement to it. This is not an argument for attempting to reverse scientific advance or technological progress; rather it is an argument for ensuring that a better balance of care is struck in any reform of the NHS. In this way, modern medicine will achieve its fullest potential. The medical profession need not become the prisoner of a market structure and values, but should use such disciplines to enhance its professional and clinical freedom. It cannot, given growing financial constraints, retain a traditional but untenable concept of total clinical freedom.

What we need is a new definition of clinical responsibility where individual judgements tailored to individual needs are married with cost-effective treatment and practice. After forty years, the present NHS structure is rightly changing and should be changed even further. It would be far better if it is changed within the framework and tradition of the NHS. An holistic approach is not a new-fangled trendy manifestation of quirky cults or way-out opinions. It is the reassertion of traditional medical values where a sensitivity to the individuality of the person is a precious part of the practice of the healing profession. Doctors must never be allowed to forget that the practice of medicine involves the whole person. Medical education has been fragmented. Responsibility for treatment has been fragmented. We have divorced the family practitioner from the hospital and medicine from the community. The responsibility for patient care has been arbitrarily divided. In consequence, we have not just fragmented the medical profession, we are in danger of fragmenting its values and its purpose.

It is time to reassert the wholeness of medicine, to do so in the way medicine is taught and practised at every level. If that is done, it will be a framework within which it is easier to combine morality and the market to provide a modern NHS.

Chapter 3

THE NURSING PROFESSION

No man, not even a doctor, ever gives any other
definition of what a nurse should be than this –
'devoted and obedient'. This definition would do just
as well for a porter. It might even do for a horse. It
would not do for a policeman . . . It seems a
commonly received idea among men, and even
among women themselves, that it requires nothing
but a disappointment in love, or incapacity in other
things, to turn a woman into a good nurse.

Florence Nightingale

Old attitudes die hard. Nevertheless, the profession of nursing
has made massive strides in the last decade. Nursing is now a
major influence on the NHS. Still not yet as influential as the
medical profession, but increasing its relative influence all the
time. Nursing is also, perhaps even more importantly, a growing
influence on the medical profession itself, its attitudes to patients
and working in a health team.

Nurses have a deeper tradition of seeing the patient in the
round, the nurse relating the patient to the house they live in,
the number of steps and stairs, the state of damp, the effectiveness, or even the existence, of central heating, a bath and the
difficulty of getting into it, whether there is an inside lavatory.
These are all vital parts of assessing patient care and are more
likely to feature high in a nurse's mind than that of a doctor.

Half of the nearly one million people who work for the NHS
are nurses – nine out of ten of these are women. Nurses' salaries
account for 22% of total expenditure on the NHS. Nurses are an
ever more important element within health care, not just in

31

hospitals but increasingly working with family doctors in primary health care. They are a key element in changing medical practice towards treating the whole person and in relating the patient and their needs to the total environment in which they live. For the good nurse, 'patients first' is not a political slogan but an all-pervading attitude capable of countering the priority given to disease by the medical profession. Few medical students' textbooks would focus on patients to the extent that most nursing textbooks do, as is well illustrated in Figure 1.[1]

Figure 1: Some members of the health care team who assist the patient and the family

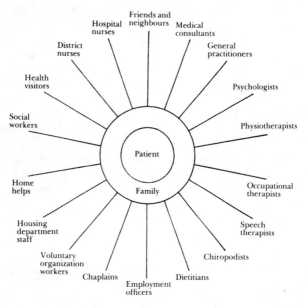

The rise in the standing and influence of the nursing profession is a new phenomenon; unlike the doctors, nurses have had to battle hard for both a justified status and a fair financial reward. They have not yet achieved either. It is only recently, with the increased authority of the Royal College of Nursing within the NHS, that nurses have been able to compare with, let alone rival, the doctors in terms of prestige and power in key decisions relating to the NHS. Fortunately, that position of professional inferiority is changing fast. But sadly, the increased value being put on the role of nurses has in part come about because of their scarcity value to the NHS. They are now seen not as marginal additions to health care but a critical ingredient which, when in short supply, restricts both the quality and the quantity of the service. In reality, nurses never were just a marginal addition; their contribution was simply too easily taken for granted. Nurses have suffered to this day from the stereotype which so upset Florence Nightingale, of 'devotion and obedience'. Those who work in the NHS know that such a stereotype is a far cry from the present day profession of nursing, but there are still echoes of these stereotypes in the presentation of nurses to the public in our newspapers and in the perception of nurses by the general public.

The key importance of nurses to the actual running of the NHS is demonstrated day by day; it no longer needs, if it ever did, strike action to make the point. It is coming to be accepted that nurses are, like everyone else in the community, interested in their standard of living and that of their families. This is not incompatible with a strong sense of vocation and dedication to patients, but it is in marked contrast to the emotional description of nurses by the popular press, summed up in headlines about 'Angels'. If we continue not to pay nurses the rate for the job, we will go on reading headlines about nurses walking out of the NHS. Nurse shortages will continue, causing the closure of wards and the cancelling of operations as Health Service managers simply find that nurses are not there to do the essential tasks. It costs £12 000 to train a registered nurse.

Most nurses leave the NHS by the age of thirty never to return. About 10% of qualified nursing staff actually leave each year. A few years ago, the NHS woke up to the fact that the shortage of nurses was becoming acute: nearly one tenth below in the funded establishment overall and a fifth below in many inner city health authorities. This was because of many factors, but few more serious than the fact that between 1981 and 1987 there was a fall of 29% in the numbers entering basic nurse training. Having trained for the NHS, one fifth do not enter the NHS to work as qualified nurses: 13% discontinue training, 2% fail their exams, 2% pass but fail to register, and 3% register but do not join the NHS. If that was not worrying enough, the demographic trend is even more alarming. By the middle 1990s, the 16–19 population will have fallen by more than a quarter from its peak in the early 1980s.

In 1986, 70 000 young women left school with between five 'O' levels, or equivalent in GCSEs, and two 'A' levels. The NHS recruited 17 000 of them. By 1993, because of the falling birth rate in the middle 1970s, it is estimated that the corresponding number of young women leaving school will be only 53 000 and the NHS will need, allowing for some growth in demand from the NHS, to recruit nearly half of them. If one wanted to be really depressed about the future, one could believe the alarming projection for Wessex RHA, which includes the counties of Hampshire and Wiltshire, the prosperous southern part of the country, that by 1996 Wessex will have to recruit 87% of all their school leavers with the requisite qualifications. It is virtually impossible for such ambitious recruitment figures to be achieved. Far more nurses will have to be retained within and won back to the NHS.

The growth of nurses in the private sector is difficult to analyse. The Independent Hospitals Association says the private sector employs 25 000 registered nurses, recruit 4000 a year, only 1500 of whom come from the NHS. But although the number of private hospital beds has not risen very fast, private nursing homes have grown very rapidly and it is in competition from private nursing homes that the NHS may find itself losing ground.

To improve retention of nurses in the NHS, the vicious circle has to be broken – an increased workload causing strain and stress, leading inevitably to professional dissatisfaction and low morale, in turn provoking a decision to leave the NHS, followed by a further increase in the workload for those remaining in the NHS, even more stress and strain and more provoked into leaving. It is also hard to exaggerate the psychological effect on a young girl at school, deciding what to do with her life, and sympathetic to a nursing career, when day after day she reads stories in the newspapers about the collapse of the NHS.

Those who cynically exploit the current problems of the NHS and yet who purport to support its purpose ought to pause and reflect upon the effect of some of their activities in creating a mood of pessimism about its future. The deficiencies of the NHS need to be dealt with away from the headlines. A determination to defuse the present crisis should be an urgent priority for anyone who fundamentally wishes the NHS well. But defusing the crisis does not mean believing that because the government has agreed to pay in full the Independent Pay Review Board's recommendations for nurses published in April 1988, the nursing shortage in the Health Service will now be solved. The shortages are very far from being corrected. The new pay structure and increases rightly concentrate on those with special skills where the shortages are greatest. These are essential changes. But it is also highly questionable whether the basic rates of pay that have been recommended will be sufficient; they owe too much to past pay differentials and not enough to future work patterns, particularly when trying to attract married women back to nursing.

Until 1982, the Whitley Council trade union negotiating machinery settled nurses' pay, but after the pay dispute in that year, the government, to its credit, agreed to set up an independent pay review body. That mechanism had been very successful in defusing the perennial doctors' pay dispute that had hitherto dogged the NHS. What was wrong was the shortsighted way in which the government altered and failed to honour the recommendation of the nurses' review body in two out of the first five years. Furthermore, in three out of these five years, the government forced the NHS to pay for part of the nurses' pay award within already committed budget allocations. That government action meant that some nurses, particularly in the traditional unions, COHSE and NUPE, were encouraged to view the pay review machinery with the same suspicion as their trade union leaders. When in 1987 the decision to pay nurses in full was announced eighteen days before the general election was called, the cynicism of many nurses was reinforced. Yet another adverse consequence of government action has been that less militant nurses have come to fear that the corollary of their pay awards will be cuts in services to patients and they have become bitter, seeing their demands, however reasonable, undermine services to patients. The government will have to show more respect for the review body's finding in 1989 and 1990, not just before the next election.

The Royal College of Nursing ballot, in 1988, once more reaffirmed the RCN's refusal to take strike action. That confirmation of the fact that nurses cannot strike without damaging patients' care has been very beneficial. It has given the review body machinery a much-needed boost as being the best mechanism for settling pay. But the RCN is treading a delicate path and its reasonableness must not be taken for granted. The review body machinery of course itself carries within it an implicit 'no strike' commitment. For that to become explicit, the independence of the review body has to be respected by government and interference must only be very much the exception.

It is interesting that Florence Nightingale drew attention to the role of the policeman when discussing the role of nurses and it is worth exploring this analogy. Policemen have been able to use their 'no strike' arrangement, enshrined in statute law, to ensure good financial rewards and retain public esteem. There are nurses, not just in the ranks of NUPE and COHSE, who fear that by endorsing a 'no strike' strategy, nurses will weaken their bargaining position. The RCN has taken a different view and it is in the interests of us all that it is proved right. To some extent, the nurses' case hitherto has been weakened by the competitive bidding for members between the different nursing unions. The doctors, by contrast, have gained through having the BMA as their dominant voice. When the medical profession was divided for a short time in the 1970s with the independent Hospital Consultants Staff Association, politicians found it easier to divide and rule. The fragmentation of nurses' representation is more a weakness for them than a strength at present.

The RCN is, however, showing every sign of moving into the new era of trade unionism far faster than the conventional trade unions and one would expect this to continue. In a sense, it appears to have decided to play the government, to use a cricketing analogy, on the same wicket, whereas the other unions are still uncertain as to whether to enter the ground. The RCN is playing cleverly within new rules but exploiting every opportunity to achieve both more money and better conditions for nurses. If the RCN strategy succeeds, as it shows every sign of doing, the risk is that the government will try to change the rules, either by unduly influencing the independence of the review board, or by reverting, in future years, to interfering with its recommendations. The RCN is entitled to make it quite clear that if the government changes the rules, then the RCN will feel free to change its attitude to strike action.

If industrial peace is to come throughout the NHS, then the independent pay review machinery wil have to be extended to all staff who work in the NHS. The next logical, and indeed urgent, extension is to put the Medical and Scientific Laboratory Organization into the pay review structure. This group has been treated badly in terms of pay, particularly when one considers that it is registered as one of the professions supplementary to medicine. Yet these scientists, unlike physiotherapists, radiographers and radiotherapists, have been deliberately kept out of the pay review procedure. This group is the most likely to undertake strike action in future years. The government is not under strong pressure to include them in the review body machinery since the predominant union is the new merged union, MFA, formed from the amalgamation of ASTMS and TASS. The leadership of these unions has always preferred to rely on traditional collective bargaining and would be most reluctant to give up implicitly or explicitly what they see as the political leverage of the strike weapon. Yet an imaginative move by the government to nip in the bud trouble in this area could herald the start of a prolonged period of industrial peace in the NHS, something which is desperately needed. Waiting lists, workload problems and staff morale would all be eased if the NHS could have a number of years free from either the threat or the reality of industrial disruption.

Yet nurses' dissatisfaction stems not just from pay. Opinion polls show that improved staffing levels are even more important to them than increased pay. Though nurses work a supposed 37½-hour week, surveys show that well over half in any one week work overtime for which they are not paid, and most do not even expect time off to compensate. Instead of working overtime as NHS employees, one in five qualified nurses takes an additional job, most working for private nursing agencies. They can then be employed in their own hospitals and even in their own wards. If they do this, they are not paid overtime rates by the agency as they would have to be if they were working for the NHS. The use of private agencies for the continued running of the NHS is a reflection on the internal management of the NHS. Many people are very cynical about private nursing agencies and their continued existence should be causing far greater concern. Periodic bouts of conscience about nursing agencies grip the media or Parliament from time to time and then subside after a few months into a complacent acceptance. Nursing agencies, unlike medical agencies, do not even operate on free market principles. They are not allowed by law to compete by paying more to the nurses they employ. What competition there is comes from the different commissions agencies charge to the hospitals. One of the chief attractions of agencies for nurses who are not working in the NHS is the flexibility they provide in working hours. It is interesting that where NHS hospitals adopt flexible working practices, there is less use of outside agencies.

To gauge the depth of feeling that exists among nurses, it is worth reflecting on how one ward sister vividly described her experience in an article in the *British Medical Journal*. Her account was part of six penetrating articles on nursing grievances,[2] the publication of which itself signalled the extent to which the medical profession has moved away from regarding the nurse as one of nature's handmaidens:

It's pay, but it's job satisfaction now too. It's cutting back on back-up staff, it's no equipment and pushing more patients into overworked wards. We can't give the nursing care that's required and that's the stress the nurses are feeling – it's the stress of not doing the job properly. Medical records staff was cut from seven to three. The nurses were expected to ring for notes, fetch and carry. They halved the number of porters. Who did the portering? The nurses. The nurses were always going to pharmacy. They cut down on domestic staff and the hours they were on the ward and the wards were always looking filthy. Because equipment was so short it was continually borrowed from ward to ward. Nurses had to walk to up to six wards to find some vital piece of equipment, like bed elevators or space blankets for patients with shock. Sometimes CSSD would run out of stock.

Every day we had too many patients for the empty beds available, so the routine admissions would be sent home – sometimes up to three times. Doctors discharged patients too early in order to get empty beds, but patients would come back again and have to be readmitted. The administration decided we could do without agency nurses so if we were short staffed we could get no one. So the nurses, who were exhausted, went off sick more often – which made for even more stress for the other nurses. Nurses were always off duty late.

Sometimes we would have three patients in one bed within a shift. One miscarriage in the night would go home at 8 a.m. Then an extra day case patient would be put into the bed. The waiting list patient who came to the ward at 10 a.m. would wait until 5 p.m. (And if the day case patient bled the waiting list patient went home and came back next morning starved for a major operation.) It was like a factory. The nurses were literally running at times we used to be so busy. So we had no satisfaction of the job being well done. Patients didn't dare talk to us because we were so busy. There was very little time for counselling.

District administrators are getting bonuses for cutting costs, bonuses for getting waiting lists shorter – they have no idea of the problem. And that made me feel even worse when I thought why we're discharging them early.

That by no means atypical account has to be set against the endless statistics quoted by government ministers about the improvement in nurses' salaries and conditions. Nurses have felt aggrieved at both Labour and Conservative governments because there has been no compensation for all the changes that have occurred surrounding nursing. Most trainee nurses used to live in subsidized hostels with reduced costs for rent and meals. That has gone as part of the inevitable move towards more independence, choice and freedom for young people. With such hostel arrangements often went subsidized travel to and from work. Also, as new hospitals began to be sited in green fields away from city centres, travel costs to work increased. This often coincided with cuts in bus services, making it almost essential to travel by car outside normal working hours. The inadequate car parking facilities at the older inner city hospitals comes up time and time again when talking to nurses. The doctors' car park is considered essential yet the nurses' car park is still a luxury. Those priorities will quickly have to change. The car park for the nurse is becoming an essential part of retaining staff, particularly when working flexible hours and attracting back into nursing young married women with children. Travelling to work at night has exposed nurses to the all too prevalent risk of being mugged. All of these factors are hard to cost and even harder to assess in terms of how they have contributed to the present exodus of nurses from the NHS. But no one visiting hospitals in the big cities and talking to nurses can be unaware that their fear of walking to the hospital at night, even when in the uniform which once gave them a respectful security, is now a major anxiety.

If nursing is to regain its popularity with school leavers, nothing is more important than better education for nurses. Education and professional status are linked. There is a long-standing professional demand from nurses for more education while still recognizing that theirs will always be a practice-based profession. This is the central theme of *Project 2000*, a report from the Central Council for Nursing, Midwifery and Health Visitors, published in 1986. The report suggests that entry qualifications should remain unchanged, but argues cogently for three divisions of labour for nursing: a 'registered practitioner', bringing together both first- and second-level nurses; a 'specialist practitioner' of a more advanced grade, involving specialist knowledge and sometimes disease-linked; and a 'helper' to act as a support worker. It is suggested that there should be an eighteen-month common foundation programme followed by an eighteen-month branch programme which would take in nursing of the child, the mentally handicapped and the mentally ill, as well as the adult. Trainee nurses, it is argued, should be seen as students. In addition much emphasis is laid on advanced educational programmes beyond registration, with closer links to higher education and a degree qualification for teachers of nursing.

These proposals must be considered alongside the demographic factors discussed earlier. Their effect would be to reduce the time that student nurses spend on the wards, where they carry much of the burden. However, without the reform and reorientation of student nursing as proposed in the *Project 2000* report, it will be very hard for the nursing profession to attract the greater proportion of young people that will be needed. *Project 2000* is highly sensible, albeit ambitious. The government has accepted it in principle, but it requires speedy implementation, for there is considerable dissatisfaction among nurses in training. A poll of student nurses in their final year has shown nearly three quarters of them seriously considered leaving the profession. Job satisfaction involves proper supervision and time for learning so that responsibility is not, as now, thrust too soon on the inexperienced.

One of the bonuses of Sir Keith Joseph's 1974 reorganization – and since there were few it is worth recalling – was that nurses were given an important role in the management of the NHS alongside administrators, treasurers and doctors. The way the First Griffiths Report on the management of the NHS was implemented in the middle 1980s was extremely damaging to the status of nurses. It appeared for a time as if they would have only a minimum managerial role within the new structure. Fortunately, it was realized that this was indefensible and, indeed, was probably not even meant to be seen to be downgrading nurses. Certainly, to deprive half the workforce of the NHS of a voice in management, at the very time when they had more to contribute to health care than at any time in the past, was an act of folly. Slowly, and still insufficiently, the potential of nurses in a management role has been re-established, but it has left permanent scars and shown how fragile is the new-found prestige of nurses, particularly within the Department of Health and Social Security.

Ministers responsible for implementing that first Griffiths Report must have dismissed the advice of the chief nursing officer in the DHSS without any regard for the consequences. It will be interesting to see how they respond to the Second Griffiths Report on community care, with its emphasis on splitting up responsibility for acute and chronic care and the possible transfer of some nursing staff from health authority to local authority employment. The report says that its recommendations may affect, but in no way diminish, the contribution that community nursing makes to community care. As an aspiration, no one can take exception to that, but its practical implementation poses many problems, as does defining the role of and responsibility for health visitors and district nurses, and the developing role of the hospice nurse, and that of the community nurse, in caring for terminally ill patients. The community psychiatric nurse is a key part of the new mental illness service and the director of the Health Advisory Service was right to stress in evidence to the House of Commons Social Services Select Committee that 'they are probably the most important single professional in the process of moving care of mental illness into the community'.[3]

Another important developing aspect of nursing that must be built up is that of the practice nurse. Although nurses have helped doctors in their surgeries since 1911, the practice nurse is a comparative newcomer, extending the service of the family doctor in a very interesting and worthwhile manner. The system of having the GP as employer recompensed 70% by the FPC has proved its worth, allowing for flexible working practices and hours. Many are married, since most practice nurses work part time, and this has meant they tend to have a maturity that allows the GP to delegate considerably to them.

An even more interesting development is to extend the role and responsibilities of the individual nurse. The report of the Community Nursing Review[4] has recommended that 'the principle should be adopted of introducing the nurse practitioner into primary health care', and that the key tasks would be to interview patients and diagnose and treat specific diseases in accordance with agreed medical guidelines, and to refer patients to GPs if there is any anxiety or if they do not fall precisely within the guidelines. It is envisaged that they should be available to conduct screening programmes for specific age groups. This represents an important step forward for nurses. There is no reason why they should not dispense prescription-only medicines in the same way that occupational nurses do, and midwives and dentists do when such medicines are essential for their practice. There is little doubt that nurse practitioners will play an ever more important role in primary care and this represents a logical extension of their professional status and competence.

Wherever one looks at the immense untapped potential for using nurses' skills and experience, it is clear that the past neglect of the nursing viewpoint and contribution is a reflection of our cultural attitude to women in decision-making roles. Who can doubt that women ought to have at least 50% of all the nominated members' positions on all RHAs and DHAs? No one can argue that women have neither the knowledge nor the experience of the NHS to take an informed view. Uniquely, the NHS has more women involved professionally than any other occupation. Medicine was one of the first professions in which women broke the male dominance. Yet women are still astonishingly under-represented in health care decision-making. There could be no better starting point for a 50% rule stipulating that no vacancy in any health authority could be filled by a man until that health authority had a minimum 50% female representation. Only by the existence of such a rule will equality of the sexes be brought on to health authorities.

The fundamental priority, whether dealing with reform of the hospital service or of primary health care, is to end nurses' traditional deference to doctors. This is important to ensure that what is established for the future is a genuine partnership of professionals working alongside each other. Nurses focus on the individual affected by illness. Doctors focus on the diagnosis and treatment. Undoubtedly nurses will do more and more physical examinations and prescribe drugs. In the US, where nurse practitioners have been prescribing for twenty years, research shows they are safe prescribers. The US experience also shows that nurse practitioners do not challenge the role of doctors but complement their skills with different skills. The extension of the nurses' role will give an added impetus to their case for more education and it will also make the task more satisfying and more attractive. At every point in the development of the NHS for the future, a particular regard will have to be paid to the views of the nursing profession. It is a resource of crucial importance.

Chapter 4

THE CREATION, STRUCTURE AND EVOLUTION OF THE NHS

Society becomes more wholesome, more serene and
spiritually healthier if it knows that its citizens have at
the back of their consciousness the knowledge that
not only themselves but also their fellows have access,
when ill, to the best that medical skill can provide.

Aneurin Bevan, *In Place of Fear*

The NHS, like most institutions in the United Kingdom, evolved. It was not just the offspring of the 1945–51 Labour government. Nevertheless, it was one of the great achievements of that post-war government. It can fairly claim to have created, in Aneurin Bevan's words, a feeling of serenity up and down the country for families faced with the anxiety and distress of illness. Ending a situation in which 'ability to pay' was the determinant of the standard of health care has been a great social advance. Only those who still remember the early years of this century can really testify to the extent to which the NHS has transformed attitudes to illness and health care. It is easy to forget how substantial that change has been.

In 1911, David Lloyd George, as Chancellor of the Exchequer, first brought forward the legislation to introduce national insurance. It was that reform which, in its essentials, dominated public and parliamentary debate about health care for the next thirty-five years. The major problem with this form of insurance-based health care was that it did not cover the whole population. Just prior to the introduction of the NHS, those

covered by compulsory health insurance schemes were still confined to manual workers and other employees earning up to
£420 a year. The scheme excluded all children, wives who did
not go out to work, the self-employed, higher-paid employees,
and many old people. Though most of those who were better off
were covered by insurance schemes entered into on a voluntary
basis, those who had no insurance cover had to contend with
both the doctor's bill and the cost of any medicines prescribed.
Though free health care was available to all schoolchildren, the
poor had to rely on a district Poor Law doctor or their local Poor
Law institution. To use these services, they had to satisfy the
relieving officer and undergo a truly humiliating means test. An
alternative was to go to the casualty department of the local
voluntary or charitable hospital which dispensed treatment that
could and should have been available from family doctors based
in the community. All too many general practitioners had two
classes of patients – those on the 'panel' who were covered by
compulsory insurance, and those who were private, fee-paying
patients. Some doctors even kept different waiting rooms for the
two classes of patients. Or, in the big cities, saw their panel
patients in lock-up surgeries while their private patients were
seen in the doctor's home.[1]

As early as 1920, the Minister of Health's Consultative Council
on Medical and Allied Services produced the Dawson Report
which asserted the then far from conventional wisdom that 'the
best means of maintaining health and curing disease should be
made available to all citizens'. In 1926, the Royal Commission on
National Health Insurance concluded, 'the ultimate solution
will lie, we think, in the direction of divorcing the medical
service entirely from the insurance system and recognizing it
along with all other public health activities as a service to be
supported from the general public funds.' This was the first
authoritative endorsement of a health service financed by the
Exchequer from general taxation. It was a view that was starting
to be held even by the British Medical Association, which was
arguing for extending the insurance principle to the dependants
of those in work and wondering how this could be financed.

The next fifteen years were characterized by an ongoing
debate on the respective roles of central and local government in

providing and coordinating health care. In 1933 the Socialist Medical Association published a report, which was influential in the Labour Party, advocating a comprehensive health service to be managed by local government under a regional planning arrangement. The conventional wisdom inside the Ministry of Health had hitherto been that the only options were either to extend national health insurance or to have the local authorities run a health service. This was challenged in 1939 when, at official level, the option of a national hospital service was first floated.

The extension of central government provision began with the outbreak of war. In 1939 the Emergency Medical Service was introduced, initially to cover air-raid casualties. This was paid for by the government with compensation being given to voluntary hospitals that took in acute cases. Gradually, as the war went on, the categories of patients for which reimbursement could be claimed from central government were extended so that by the end of the war hospitals were increasingly financed through claims on central government. Whereas in 1938, 34% of the income of the London hospitals came from donors and only 8% from public authorities, by 1947, 16% of their income came from donors and 46% was coming from public authorities. By then, local authorities provided most of the hospitals for the chronic sick, infectious diseases, mental illness and mental handicap, over one tenth of these beds being for tuberculosis and other infectious diseases. A few local authorities, like the London County Council (LCC), Birmingham City, Surrey and Middlesex, developed impressive acute hospital services. But apart from obstetrics, where local authority hospitals nationwide provided most of the beds, provision was very uneven. Local authority hospitals also tended to be very strict about only treating their own residents. In total, local authority hospitals provided about four fifths of all kinds of hospital beds, but their reputation was low and their standards were patchy.

In March 1943, Ernest Brown, then Minister of Health in the wartime coalition, presented proposals to Parliament for a unified health care system with a central government department, advised by a central council, and based on a system of large local government areas formed either by joint authorities or with a regional structure. The opposition to this plan from the medical profession was particularly strong since it felt that the proposals were too similar to those put forward by the National Association of Local Government Officers and the Society of Medical Officers of Health.

In February 1944, the new Minister of Health, Sir Henry Willink, produced a White Paper which modified some of the earlier proposals but retained the idea that the local organization of all the services should be vested in joint authorities advised by an appointed council. The White Paper suggested that general practitioners should be under contract to a central medical board, though this was later changed to a local committee based on the national health insurance system. Prime Minister Winston Churchill had little enthusiasm for the White Paper and wanted to delay its publication, but Lord Woolton, who was Minister of Reconstruction, wrote to Churchill defending the White Paper as 'a compromise which is far more favourable to the Conservatives than to Labour ministers and when it is published I expect more criticism from the left than from Conservative critics'. The controversy over whether to impose health centres where general practitioners would practise was strongly fought within the coalition. In the White Paper it was fudged.

In June 1945, after the coalition ended, Sir Henry Willink, still Minister of Health but now a member of Churchill's Conservative caretaker government, conceded to the medical profession an even lower profile for health centres, no direction for GPs, and regional bodies. All of this the doctors wanted and it balanced other concessions to local government. Willink had achieved a substantial measure of agreement for his proposals. Not surprisingly, local government liked the proposals, for though he advocated regional councils, these were to be concerned with mainly hospital and specialist services and in an advisory capacity. Local government still retained executive powers and the voluntary hospitals retained their separate identity. The idea of a unified service had been abandoned.

Yet when, in March 1946, the 'National Health Service Bill – Summary of the Proposed New Service' was presented to Parliament, local government felt let down. Aneurin Bevan's major new proposal was that ownership of all the hospitals and the organization of consultant services of all kinds should be transferred to regional hospital boards. This established what became known as the tripartite structure – a hospital service, local authority health services, and the general medical services administered through executive councils. The Conservative Party, now in opposition, abandoned any pretence of being in favour of a national health service. The BMA, when confronted with a practical scheme for the implementation of such a service, fought a highly reactionary campaign against the legislation. The BMA concentrated in particular, as any trade union would, on the concerns of the majority of its members, the general practitioners.

The medical profession was, in fact, not opposed to Aneurin Bevan's most distinctive contribution, namely the integration of the municipal local-authority-run and voluntary-run hospitals. The opposition to that proposal came within the Labour cabinet from Herbert Morrison, as always the defender of local government who was, not unreasonably, proud of his own record, as leader of the LCC, in providing many good acute hospitals for Londoners. The Bevan–Morrison argument reflected a long, historic battle within the Labour Party between the 'centralists' and the 'decentralists'. Though centralist or state socialism has been the path which Labour has trodden in Britain, in many other countries, socialist or social democratic parties have chosen the decentralist path. But Bevan was rightly influenced by the appalling Poor Law hospitals over the country as a whole, and perhaps particularly influenced by the peculiarly bad provision of hospitals in his native Wales. Morrison argued in a memorandum to cabinet colleagues that, 'If the Regional Boards and District Committees are to be subject to the Minister's directions on all questions of policy, they will be mere creatures of the Ministry of Health with little vitality of their own.' He went on to admit, 'Yet it is difficult under a State system to envisage the alternative situation in which, in order to give them vitality they are left free to spend money without the Minister's approval.'

The search for that missing ingredient, vitality in the running of the NHS, has continued throughout its forty years and is with us still today. Fashions come and go as to how to administer the

NHS. More democracy is flavour of the year one moment, more management the next. Aneurin Bevan pleased the doctors by coming out against local democratic control at the outset, but that did not stop them challenging other aspects. His real fight with the BMA came over his insistence that he, as Minister of Health, should control the distribution of GPs, that the sale of GP practices should cease and that GPs should be salaried employees. That last point was a red rag to a bull as far as the BMA was concerned. It was determined to maintain the doctor's independence. In April 1948, GPs threatened to withdraw their labour and by so doing hoped to prevent the NHS from coming into being on the appointed day of 5 July of that year. There was a crisis of authority. Questions were asked as to who governed the country. Bevan promised amending legislation to make it clear that the government would not insist on a wholetime salaried GP service. Even so, a poll of BMA members showed that overall 54% were against further discussion with the minister. The GPs were 2:1 against while the consultants, whom Bevan had been at pains to buy off, split 50:50. It was a testing time for the Minister of Health, and in handling the situation, he showed considerable political skill and a hitherto unnoticed talent for political compromise.

Aneurin Bevan's friends covered a wide social range. He enjoyed the company of talented people with whom he might have little in common politically. This characteristic enabled him to wheel and deal across a very broad spectrum of medical opinion. He knew he would not beat the GPs unless he could buy off the consultants, and he did precisely that with a salary structure and merit awards that allowed him to boast that he had 'stuffed their mouths with gold'. The BMA revolt collapsed despite being encouraged at every turn by the Conservative opposition. On 5 July 1948, the NHS was in business.

A national dental service has always been part of the NHS and for dentists the free check-up has been a cornerstone of the NHS. A dental screening service has been a statutory duty since 1918. It has hitherto been obligatory for the Community Dental Service to carry out this task through the health authorities. The government's recent removal of that obligation to provide for inspection and treatment of children is very serious. Dentistry is an area where there has been greater erosion of the principles of the National Health Service than any other part of the service. The NHS, however, still accounts for approximately 90% of dentistry in the United Kingdom, 70% of that being in general dental practice. Charges which in 1968 provided for 19% of the total cost of the NHS General Dental Services, in 1988 provide for more than 30%. The government will argue that all this shows that increasing charges has no bad effects, for in dentistry preventive health has achieved considerable success. The caries rate, or the number of teeth that need filling, is falling markedly – but fluoride toothpaste is probably the main reason for this. Dentists are now spending more time treating periodontal disease; teeth are being retained longer and the number of elderly who are without teeth is declining sharply. Much of this is probably due to early diagnosis and encouraging patients to attend for a quick free check-up. It is probably only in fifty years' time that we will be able to assess the cost in medical and dental terms of abandoning the free check-up. When this starts, it will be even more important to make more effort to market dentistry. This is especially the case among the 50% of the population who rarely, if ever, attend. Government policies towards advertising will probably result in more aggressive advertising by individual dentists and this is to be welcomed, for it may increase the coverage of dentistry and the dental workload.

The present system of payment, however, encourages high volume but not invariably high-quality dentistry. There is also far too little incentive for individual dentists working in the Health Service to adopt a preventive approach. Patient charges are too high and are now 75% of total, with a maximum patient charge of £150.00 for a course of treatment. Every time charges are raised substantially, there is a detectable downturn in the number of treatments. Though the long-term growth in the volume of treatment – running at about 4.7% per year – continues, it continues at a lower level and there is a downward step in the graph after each increase. The same will happen for attendances for check-ups. The number of dentists on the register is increasing rapidly due to the expansion of dental student places in the 1960s and 1970s, and with the dentist:patient ratio becoming more favourable, it should be possible to improve the quality of work done. Areas without enough dentists still exist, particularly in certain rural areas, and the inequalities in provision will now be likely to continue since it is felt that there is an over-production of dental graduates. This is, however, based on existing patterns of up-take and treatment. Regardless of the opportunity for improving the service, the dental student intake is being reduced by 20% and a cut of 10% has already been implemented. A further 10% cut is due in the next two years as a result of the UGC decision to close Dundee and University College, London, dental schools. It will, however, be some years before the full effects of this decision are felt.

It is medically and scientifically indefensible to treat dental health differently from other aspects of health care. We know that the earlier an oral cancer is identified, the higher the cure rate. A patient with oral ulceration is treated free if he or she goes to a doctor. Now they will have to pay if they go to the dentist. Nor is the current method of payment for general dental practitioners within the Health Service the best. At present, it is item-by-service, although a pilot scheme is in operation to see how a capitation system would work. There is much to be said for bringing the dental practitioner more into line with the general medical practitioner in relation to both their pattern of payment and working practice. This could evolve over time if dentistry were placed firmly within the mainstream of developments in the NHS.

The decision to allow the GPs to remain independent contractors with a capitation payment system was probably inevitable. To this day, GPs prize their independence and believe that they benefit from what is, in theory, a state-funded market system of payment. Yet the General Medical Services Committee of the BMA has wrongly sought to limit the market and inhibit competition. It has resisted advertising and acted to reduce opportunities for GPs to compete for patients. The capitation system does, nevertheless, mean that patients are theoretically free to choose their own doctor, though in many parts of the country this is not easily done. The most serious side effect of their independent contractor status has been that GPs have remained, to this day, separate from the hospital service. As a consequence, GPs plough their own furrow; some more by accident than design, some quite deliberately. The consequences of this separation between hospital and family doctoring are profound.

Successive governments, always conscious of Bevan's struggles, have felt unable to confront the GPs' negotiators and bring the hospital and family practitioner services together. The first two decades of the NHS mostly saw a Conservative government locked in battle with the medical profession over pay. Enoch Powell, formerly a Conservative Health Minister, reflecting later on his own dealings with the doctors, wrote: 'the unnerving discovery every Minister of Health makes at or near the outset of his term of office is that the only subject he is ever destined to discuss with the medical profession is money.'[2]

It was not until the first report of the Review Body on Doctors' and Dentists' Remuneration in December 1971 that the politics was taken out of the medical professions' annual salary controversy. A similar provision was eventually introduced for nursing staff, midwives, health visitors and professions allied to medicine, in July 1983. It will probably turn out that a similar mechanism eventually covers the salary levels of all those who work in the NHS. Some of the trade union leaders will be reluctant to give up their so-called free collective bargaining rights, but those who work in the NHS will see this mechanism as the one that avoids their being thrust into strike action and ensures broad comparability across the NHS for people doing the same type of work.

The National Health Service Act 1946 laid a duty on the Minister of Health to 'promote the establishment in England and Wales of a comprehensive Health Service designed to secure improvement in the physical and mental health of the people of England and Wales', and the service had to be available to all citizens. A similar duty was laid on the responsible minister in Scotland.

The service was divided into three parts. It was this division which ensured the continued dominance of hospitals and acute medicine and surgery, and an insufficient emphasis on preventive health as well as the perpetuation of the pattern of institutional care for the elderly, mentally ill and mentally handicapped:

a hospital and specialist services
b local health authority services
c executive council services for general and dental practitioners.

That structure remained unchanged until 1974, though it came to be increasingly questioned. In 1956, the Guillebaud Report, which was enquiring into the cost of the NHS, concluded, much to people's surprise, that expenditure had decreased relative to GNP from 3¾% to 3¼%. However, a dissenting minority report on structure by Sir John Maude, who was later to chair the royal commission into local government, wanted unification under local government. Even the doctors, in a report under the chairmanship of a distinguished surgeon, Sir Arthur Porritt, urged unification of the administrative tiers in principle, but under an autonomous health authority.

On 6 November 1967, Kenneth Robinson, Labour's Minister of Health, made a statement to the House of Commons in which he said that he had begun a full and careful examination of the administrative structure, looking ten or twenty years ahead, and that he was 'aware that some people say that the tripartite structure is unwieldy and that to have three types of separate authority is not the right way to achieve that degree of integration which a proper service to the individual requires'. He wanted this study to proceed in parallel with the royal commission studying local government in England and the Seebohm Committee considering the local-authority-allied personal services in England and Wales. He also hoped to have proposals about the administration of the medical and related services ready so that they could be looked at alongside the recommendations of the Royal Commission on Medical Education which was then sitting.

Even then, I and others writing about unifying the NHS were far from certain that either Kenneth Robinson or the government was ready to face down the reluctance of the medical profession to cross these seemingly impenetrable administrative barriers.[3] The structure of the NHS had been described as 'a piece of administrative machinery, the ideas of which belong to the age of Victoria'. The sum total of its parts in England amounted to 15 regional hospital boards, 336 hospital management committees, 134 executive councils controlling the affairs of 22 000 GPs, and 174 local health authorities. Labour recognized then, as it had recognized years before, that there was no hope of persuading the medical profession to accept integrating the Health Service under the control of local government.

Relations with the medical profession were still fraught; Labour, in 1964, coming into government after thirteen years of Conservative rule, had faced – through no fault of their own – the need for immediate negotiations with the family doctors. An angry BMA was then already holding in reserve resignations from 18 000 doctors. Many GPs were not bluffing and were ready to leave the NHS entirely. Fortunately, the new pay structure Kenneth Robinson negotiated with the general practitioners in 1966, usually referred to as the Family Doctor Charter, revived the prestige and standing of general practice. Health centres began to be built, the BMA's demand that the major method of payment should be by item-by-service was dropped in exchange for specific payments for night visits and such items as vaccinations and immunization. The capitation system was also changed to allow for a salary element, a basic allowance, with incentives to help recruitment to under-doctored areas. The independent contractor status was, however, not changed.

Yet Kenneth Robinson's Green Paper in 1968 did bridge the divide between the hospitals and GPs, proposing unification on the basis of forty to fifty area health boards and the abolition of regional health boards. In 1970, Richard Crossman, Secretary of State in the new Department of Health and Social Security (DHSS), produced another Green Paper. This was done mainly because the Royal Commission on Local Government had, to everyone's surprise, recommended ninety local authorities, and it was felt right to advocate ninety area health authorities to ensure coterminosity across boundaries. Crossman, however, brought back a regional element with fourteen regional health councils meant to have planning rather than executive responsibility. He also introduced the concept of a mixed membership for the health authorities, with one third plus the chairman appointed by the Secretary of State, one third appointed by the local authority, and one third appointed by the health professions.

It was left, however, to Sir Keith Joseph, the new Conservative Secretary of State, to reorganize the NHS, publishing a White Paper in 1972, and ensuring that the National Health Service Reorganization Act was given royal assent on 5 July 1973, twenty-five years to the day after the NHS started. This reorganization brought local authority health services into new area health authorities, but left the GPs with their own administrative vehicle, now renamed the family practitioner committees (FPCs) but working under the new area health authorities. The deadline for implementation of the new structure was 1 April 1974. In fact, Labour won the election in February 1974.

Barbara Castle was the new Secretary of State for Social Services and I was her Minister of Health. We actually considered halting the whole reorganization, but concluded, wisely in retrospect, that we had no alternative but to implement legislation which we had, in important respects, opposed in the House of Commons. Inflation was rising, eventually reaching 27% in 1975. The Health Service was hard enough to run without us attempting to reverse the reorganization. Full implementation had been planned to take until 1976, but the teething problems were immense. The reforms were flawed in many respects: not only had the concept of an executive regional health authority been reintroduced, but there was a new additional tier of administrative districts to operate, in many cases, under the ninety area health authorities for England. We modified one small element of these proposals, giving a slight tilt towards greater democratic accountability by increasing the local authority membership of the coterminous area health authorities to one third, and strengthening the newly created community health councils, giving them both money and staff. It would undoubtedly have caused chaos if we had tried at that late stage to remove a tier of administration, as we were tempted to do.

The traumatic experience of 1974–6, in dealing with all the problems of such a major upheaval as a national reorganization, has made me, and many others who worked within the NHS at that time, deeply sceptical of a further wholesale administrative reform of the NHS. Another politically contested reorganization does not provide the answer to the problems of the NHS. The incoming Conservative government in 1979 had, over the previous few years in opposition, totally distanced themselves from their own administrative creation. They even vigorously criticized the fact that 16 700 extra administrative staff had been recruited by 1977, trying unfairly to pin the responsibility for this on to the Labour government. In 1976, the NHS was in one of its periodic moods of introspection associated with a public sense of crisis. The nurses' pay dispute, though generously resolved by the Halsbury awards, poisoned the atmosphere and exacerbated the pay-bed dispute with the consultants. Inflation was cutting monthly into health authority budgets. The Prime Minister, Harold Wilson, then resorted to one of his favourite devices for cooling a controversial situation: a royal commission was appointed.

The Royal Commission on the NHS, the membership of which had been carefully chosen, reported to the new Conservative government in July 1979. It was not as critical of the NHS as some Conservatives within the government had hoped. The commissioners concluded,[4] 'We are all too conscious that our report will be disappointing to those who have been looking to us for some blinding revelation which would transform the NHS. Leaving to one side our non-capacity for revelation of this kind, we must say as clearly as we can that the NHS is not suffering from a mortal disease susceptible only to heroic surgery. Already the NHS has achieved a great deal and embodies aspirations and ideals of great value. The advances to be made – which undoubtedly will be made – will be brought about by constant application and vigilance.' This judgement is still relevant today. The royal commission did, however, conclude that there was one tier of administration too many and recommended that the structure should be slimmed down.

In December 1979, the government, in a document entitled 'Patients First', set in motion the removal of the area health authority tier completely. This was to be done by giving districts autonomy and establishing individual statutory authorities. Legislation followed and by April 1982 the NHS had had its second, though not as traumatic as the first, reorganization. That was followed by the NHS management enquiry, otherwise known as the First Griffiths Report, published in October 1983, which swept aside Sir Keith Joseph's consensus management. The Joseph structure had basically involved the input of a doctor, nurse, treasurer and administrator working as a team. The management enquiry concluded in favour of a single general manager to operate at unit, district and regional level. This was to be accompanied by a Health Services supervisory board to be chaired by the Secretary of State, and a management board accountable to it with an executive chairman. Sir Roy Griffiths himself, then deputy managing director of Sainsbury's, suggested that the chairman of the management board should come from neither the civil service nor from within the NHS. Implementation of all this followed in June 1984. Legislation was enacted in 1985 for separate family practitioner committees, mostly with larger boundaries than the district health authorities (DHAs), and no longer nominally part of the health authority structure. The FPCs are now better managed, moving towards full computerization. The cervical cytology call and recall system, the medical surgery inspection programme and a new pharmacy contract have all been introduced. More and more FPCs are appointing health promotion officers. All these are steps in the right direction, but do not grapple with the division between family doctors and hospital doctors.

In effect, the Conservative government of Edward Heath had imposed one administrative structure, only to be followed within ten years by the imposition of a totally different administrative structure by the Conservative government of Margaret Thatcher. It is no wonder that those who work in the NHS are sceptical about politicians' reforms and about lectures from politicians about efficiency and management. The administrative structure of the NHS, despite all that change, had still not been unified. The hospital and community services remained separate from the family practitioner services, the administrative boundaries and the financial boundaries now being in most cases totally different. It can be argued in defence of the then government that, given the certain resistance of the GPs to anything which they see as threatening their much-vaunted independence they had to fight shy, as in the past, of bringing the FPCs within the district health authorities in any meaningful way. Governments also avoid making district health authorities, not RHAs, responsible for consultants' contracts. Yet both of these artificial divisions count seriously against the efficient running of the NHS and must be challenged.

The restricted attempt in 1988 to impose cash limits on some aspects of the family practitioner committee budgets could be the starting point. It is quite possible that GPs will become more receptive to change when cash limits really start to bite. The government will begin to use its general power taken in the 1988 legislation to bring the entire FPC budget under control. At present, for example, the cost of drugs prescribed by GPs is outside any cash limit. In England in 1986/7, the gross cost to the family practitioner services of the drugs prescribed was £1378 million and this was entirely demand-led. Hospital doctors have operated under cash limits for years. But they have got around the cash limits on their own drug spending by off-loading much of their prescribing costs on to the FPCs. They now refer the patient back to their GP for all follow-on prescriptions. In part as a consequence, hospital prescribing cost only £318 million for 1986/7. Yet GPs will find that if they accept cash limits on their FPC budget, this will be extremely restricting. In England in 1986, for example, excluding prescribing costs, gross payments made to GPs for the provision of general medical services was £1131 million. They would find it much easier if their DHA budget was linked to that of the FPC, for hospital spending accounts for over 70% of all NHS costs, total revenue expenditure on hospital services being £8255 million in 1986/7.

The logic of placing cash limits on GPs is hard to deny when all other aspects of NHS expenditure have cash limits. The Treasury has been wanting to make this change for years. All that is happening in 1988 is that the government is implementing the placing of cash limits on GPs in stages in order to lessen the outcry from GPs. It will soon become clear to the BMA negotiators that it is not in the interests of GPs to let a cash limit be applied purely to their own budget. Undoubtedly, what they need are FPCs with the same boundaries as the district health authorities. GPs would continue to be independent contractors, paid in exactly the same way as at present. The FPC would be a statutory committee of the DHA, but its budget would be part of the DHA budget. This would tend to maximize the cost-effectiveness of treatment and make for an informed choice as to whether treatment should be undertaken in hospital by the consultant, or at home by the GP. For the first time, it would put GPs and hospital consultants in the same professional and financial basket. It would give a financial incentive to look at preventive medicine and foster health maintenance attitudes. GPs would be answerable to their colleagues in hospital for their cost decisions, just as hospital consultants who control far larger budgets would be answerable to GPs for their cost decisions.

This would provide a very powerful reassessment of medical priorities and be far more likely to achieve the much-needed redistribution of resources from the hospital services to primary health care. Producing that redistribution has so far eluded all governments. It cannot come from DHSS circulars; it needs the formidable professional pressure of the GPs, who time and time again have shown themselves to be readier than the hospital consultants to consider the health of the whole person and to shift medical priorities towards preventive medicine. This linkage of FPCs with DHAs is the one administrative change which the NHS cannot escape; it need not be too disruptive, particularly if it is done with some of the other changes discussed in Chapter 8 on community care.

The NHS, though governed by the same principles throughout, is in fact organized somewhat differently between England, Wales, Scotland and Northern Ireland. The Secretary of State for Social Services is responsible for the NHS in England, while in Wales, Scotland and Northern Ireland, that function is performed by their respective Secretaries of State. These four cabinet ministers are directly accountable to Parliament. The statutory health authorities and boards are, however, charged under legislation with specific duties. The members of these authorities are appointed by ministers or nominated by local authorities rather than being directly elected. In England, the NHS Management Board has started to bring the professional health administrators into the centre, advising ministers direct. But from all reports, these boards have not yet developed either the authority or the influence to change the dominating role of the civil servants in the DHSS or that of the RHAs in relation to the DHAs.

If the NHS could be given financial autonomy with its own independent health fund, as described in Chapter 10, Paying for the NHS, there is a strong case for using existing legislative powers to create a special health authority out of the supervisory board. It would then be possible to vest in that national health authority the executive responsibility for the running of the whole NHS in England, instead of having that exercised as at present by the DHSS. It is not worth doing this, however, unless it could coincide with a separate, identifiable health service budget, freed from normal Treasury controls. This would also stop ministers in the DHSS being answerable for all the detailed aspects of the running of the NHS. This continually sucks ministers into the day-to-day running of the NHS and, once sucked in, the DHSS stays involved. The accountability of ministers to Parliament is greatly exaggerated for its democratic value and very costly in centralizing the service. Redefining a purely strategic role for ministers in the DHSS is an important part of any overall reform package.

In England, there are fourteen regional health authorities responsible for hospital and community services. The 191 district health authorities are responsible to the regions, and twenty special health authorities – covering a wide range of post-graduate teaching hospitals like the Royal Marsden and the Hospital for Sick Children at Great Ormond Street, and the Mental Health Act Commission and Health Education Authority – are all directly accountable to the DHSS.

The RHAs currently have three distinct roles: to allocate funds from central government to district health authorities; to set regional strategy and policy so that the most effective use can be made of resources, and to ensure that all areas of health care are adequately provided across regions; and to provide common services, taking advantage of economies of scale.

The most important function of the region is to allocate money to the districts. This has become even more crucial since money has been allocated differentially to regional health authorities, for this makes their decisions on allocation within their region both difficult and important in terms of carrying the redistribution of resources right down to where it affects patients. In May 1975, as Minister of Health, I established the Resource Allocation Working Party (RAWP), 'To review the arrangements for distributing NHS capital and revenue . . . with a view to establishing a method of securing . . . a pattern of distribution responsive objectively, equitably and efficiently . . . to relative need . . .' Even at the time, we knew we were embarking on one of the most profound changes in the development of the NHS.

When the working party reported in September 1976, the amazingly rapid growth rate that the NHS had just experienced – nearly 1% of GDP in just over two years – was about to end and indeed largely to be clawed back with the expenditure cutbacks imposed by the IMF. Redistribution of resources to the RHAs in future, we knew, was going to have to take place against a less buoyant economic background both nationally and within the NHS. Nevertheless, RAWP was structured from an objective analysis of facts, though its creation owed almost everything to a political stimulus. The working party was deliberately designed to provide an apolitical way forward that would withstand changes of ministers and governments. So it has proved to be. The RAWP recommendations have been implemented by Labour and Conservative governments, despite the powerful protests of the London teaching hospitals. Notwithstanding the difficult economic circumstances, there has been measurable progress in correcting inequalities.

Given the rigidities and inequalities existing before RAWP, this progress has been perhaps the most radical development in the NHS and far more beneficial to the NHS than all the varying reorganizations of its administration. In 1979–80, the poorest region was 9% below its RAWP target allocation, the richest 13% above. For 1984–5, by contrast, the range was 5% below to 9% above. The comparison between the position in 1976 with the wide discrepancies then and the position by 1987 is well illustrated in Table 2, overleaf. There have been quantifiable improvements in the services provided in the West Midlands and the North East as a direct result of RAWP. It has, however, caused difficulties in other regions, particularly the Thames regions, as redistribution has taken place at a time when there has been little if any real growth there in health spending. The RAWP formula has

Table 2: **National regional RAWP positions 1976 and 1987**

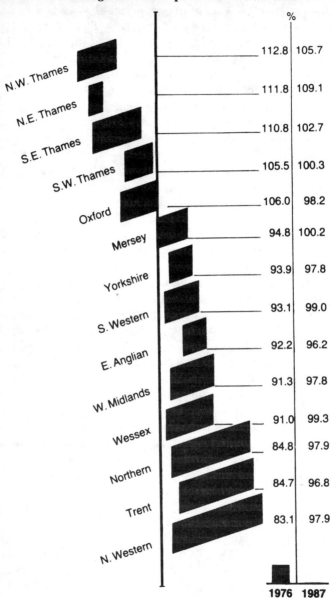

	%	
	112.8	105.7
N.W. Thames	111.8	109.1
N.E. Thames	110.8	102.7
S.E. Thames	105.5	100.3
S.W. Thames	106.0	98.2
Oxford	94.8	100.2
Mersey	93.9	97.8
Yorkshire	93.1	99.0
S. Western	92.2	96.2
E. Anglian	91.3	97.8
W. Midlands	91.0	99.3
Wessex	84.8	97.9
Northern	84.7	96.8
Trent	83.1	97.9
N. Western	**1976**	**1987**

rightly been modified over time and while, in theory, it compensates for patients being treated out of their home districts there are still a number of distortions and disincentives. The 'service increment for teaching' (SIFT) has helped compensate for the extra service cost per medical student and, to some extent, drawn the teeth of the London teaching hospitals' criticisms, but in hindsight it must be said that relying on standardized morbidity ratios as a proxy for mortality data was inevitably somewhat rough and ready. What is remarkable is how well the criteria have withstood the testing of time, though it is disappointing how much the reallocation process has been slowed down since 1986.

It was reasonable to expect that the NHS, from 1948 on, would have redressed the uneven distribution of the capital stock that it had inherited and which had arisen haphazardly over the centuries. Inexplicably, very little was done to redistribute resources in the NHS for twenty-five years. The regions seemed to be content to accept the historic pattern and ministers were unwilling to rock the boat. The spread of health care provision in the regions around the national average was about 50% in 1948 and yet this variation was, incredibly, still the same in 1973, though Wales had by then risen to a position above, instead of below, the English regional average. In England, expenditure per head on hospital services varied between the Trent region with the lowest and the North East Thames region with the highest. The situation was truly outrageous, given that redressing inequalities was meant to be one of the major reasons for bringing to an end the fragmented and uneven standards of hospital provision that characterized the situation before 1948 and creating a state-run hospital service in the first place.

The problem now is that though there has been a spectacular redistribution of resources in the regions, generally speaking from the south to the north, there has not yet been as much quantifiable progress in correcting inequalities between districts. Once the regional health authority receives its revenue allocation for the coming year from the DHSS, normally early in the calendar year, it has to determine how this should be distributed to its districts. Internally, it has to divert money for its own regional services, such as the blood transfusion services, and cover its administrative costs, and then it has to take account of projects already in progress in the districts. A formula can redistribute money but it takes a long time to affect the distribution of buildings; also, the resistance to switching existing patterns of employment is considerable. There is a delicate balance to strike between on the one hand ensuring that patients have comprehensive services near to them, so they do not have to travel too far, and on the other hand not obliging each and every district health authority to become fully self-sufficient. Self-sufficiency as an aim in itself is a recipe for an inefficient and costly Health Service. The boundaries of DHAs can never be perfectly matched to natural communities and it will continue to be necessary to strike a reasonable balance between the historic distribution and a fair distribution of resources.

The most important modification of the initial RAWP formula was made in 1985–6, when it moved from the historical two-year-old population factor to a projected population for the year of the allocation. This made RAWP more responsive to movements of population. Cross-boundary flows between districts to reflect patient movements were incorporated in 1987. The problems associated with any formula are considerable. RAWP cannot yet reflect the different costs of treating different clinical conditions. There is doubt about the significance of the relationship in the standardized mortality rates (SMRs) and morbidity, or even that there is a linear relationship between SMRs and needs. Although the teaching hospital factor helps the four London regions, they have the additional argument that they are not fully compensated for the higher labour costs in the capital. But the regions in the north of the country counter this by noting that economic and social deprivation is not taken into account as reflected in their high unemployment figures and the numbers of single-parent families. Nevertheless, the RAWP formula has won a wider acceptance within the NHS than any of us ever expected when we embarked on the change.

The challenge now is to develop acceptable techniques for redistributing resources between the DHAs. This will become increasingly important if we are steadily to adopt an internal market as I argue we should in Chapter 6, A Market in Health. At present RHAs allocate to DHAs using their own distinctive criteria and do not all use the same modified formula derived from RAWP. They would argue that this is the only way to reflect the considerable differences in size and in provision that exist between some DHAs. Yet gradually a more unified standard is being applied. It is hard to escape the conclusion that some of the arbitrariness in the present decision-making stems from the RHAs feeling the need to justify their existence. Though the existence of the RHAs shields ministers from some of the complaints of the DHAs and provides a semi-political buffer between the parliamentary hothouse and the coalface, it also perpetuates another, and many think unnecessary, tier to the NHS. The regions can operate without paying much attention to government priorities. The classic documented proof of this was in the late 1970s–early 1980s when most of them diverted the £3 million that I had allocated to them in 1976 for building regional security units for the mentally disturbed criminal population to other health projects – a fact discovered by parliamentary scrutiny of health budgets.

If an internal market between DHAs develops, so the role for the RHAs should diminish. But an internal market will highlight anomalies within RAWP, such as the fact that it does not adjust forout patient and day patient caseflows, and this could become a disincentive to the more widespread introduction of outpatient and day care treatments. Therefore, for an internal market to operate, there needs to be a sensitive mechanism for allocating resources to districts. If regional health authorities did not exist, these functions would have to be carried out direct from the DHSS. There is no indication that this would either improve the situation at local level or reduce costs. To try to handle 191 DHAs would require the DHSS itself to reorganize, and without doubt it would expand in order to do so.

The present system could, however, be improved and streamlined without structural change, although legislation would be required to abolish categories of membership. There is some uncertainty about the future relationships between DHAs and district officers, and RHAs and regional officers, and also the relationships between district chairmen and regional chairmen and ministers, when there is meant to be a further decentralization of power. The nature of autonomous regional authorities is that they will not easily divest themselves of power and functions. They will, as they have done for the last forty years, resist serious decentralization to the DHAs. The RHA needs to be the servant of its DHAs, not the master. Regional health authority membership should be changed so that RHAs become a forum for district health authority chairmen who would elect their own regional chairman. This could be matched by a regional management board of district general managers. The regional health authorities would then operate with executive powers and only a small secretariat to allocate funds for regional services and to set regional strategy, policy and capital programmes. Common services would be handled on a consortium basis by all or a number of district or special health authorities.

In this way, DHAs would be both more understanding and more supportive of decisions made at regional level, since decisions would be seen to directly reflect local needs. Apart from the saving of present regional health authority membership costs, there would also be a slim-down of RHA staff, district health authorities having a vested interest in its being as small and effective as possible. Perhaps more importantly, however, it would mean that the decisions made at regional level are 'owned' by district health authorities, and some of the tension that currently exists would be reduced.

District health authorities vary considerably, both in population and size, and there is still scope for some rationalization towards a rather larger size. The 1974 attempt to make health authorities coterminous with local government social services departments having been abandoned, the largest district is Leicestershire, with a population of 836 000, and there are a few small districts of under 100 000, most being in the range of 250 000–300 000 population. Budgets vary considerably too, though most are in the range of £30–£60 million. By any standards, a district health authority is a big business. In many towns and cities, they are the largest single employer. Every DHA has a community health council (CHC) acting as a consumer watchdog financed by a fixed sum from the RHA to ensure its independence.

Since 1985, in England and Wales, family practitioner committees have been autonomous statutory public bodies. Yet an important precedent for those who want to see amalgamation of FPCs with the DHAs is Scotland, where there is no separate administration. General medical and dental practitioners, pharmacists and opticians have contracts directly with the health boards and there is no loss of independence.

In Wales, spending on health per head has in the past been higher than in England but is now much the same. There is no RHA, but nine DHAs, each reporting direct to the Secretary of State for Wales. In Scotland, spending per head is 15% higher than in England and in Wales. There is no RHA, but there is a Common Service Agency to administer ambulance and blood transfusion services and also major building projects. There are health boards reporting to the Secretary of State for Scotland through the Scottish Home and Health Department.

In Northern Ireland, spending on the Health Service is considerably higher than in any other part of the UK. If the Northern Ireland budget were allocated using the English RAWP formula, it would have to fall by a sixth. There is no regional tier, but a Central Services Agency which takes over the FPC function and four area health and social services boards with subordinate units or districts. The combining of health and social services in Northern Ireland has, on the face of it, much to recommend it and has been rather envied. Performance, however, has not yet fulfilled expectations. Yet experience in Northern Ireland does, as the Social Services Committee of the House of Commons Report on Community Care says, 'offer a glimpse of a long-term outcome'.[5] It would require much too large an administrative upheaval to reintroduce coterminous health and social services boundaries in England, let alone to bring social services departments into a DHA. That should be considered when and if we move towards an all-purpose, single-tier local government structure. Some have talked of creating a special community care authority linking the FPC with social services departments. But this would retain the division between primary health care and hospitals, cause considerable administrative upheaval, and be much resented by local government as yet another reduction in its powers. Also, the removal from local democratic control of sensitive personal services that impact on other local authority functions would be seen as a further indirect extension of the powers of central government.

Most people within the NHS shudder at talk of further reorganization – and with some justice. But as has been said by a director of social services, 'If you wanted to create a structure for health and social services that inhibited cooperation and led to misunderstanding and inertia, you could not do better than reinvent the present structure.'[5] Nevertheless, the limited changes suggested here would be part of a process of slow evolution, not incompatible with more radical change later. It would be best done through pilot schemes to iron out any teething problems, before being implemented England-wide, to create a more effective structure.

Gradually, the civil service input into the NHS should be reduced, and the NHS freed to develop as an independent health authority. Initially, this can happen within the DHSS while retaining full responsibility to the Minister of Health. For the present, as is argued at the end of Chapter 8 on community care, creating a Minister for Community Care is all that is needed. If the NHS can start to become more autonomous, the more far-reaching possibility of a legislatively separate health authority eventually being given total autonomy, rather like the BBC, is well worth considering. It would be meaningless, however, until its finances were autonomous as well, and that is why the discussion about creating a separate health fund in Chapter 10 is so important. Professional health administrators should increasingly be the staff of the DHSS, leaving a minimum of civil servants to deal with the demands of Whitehall's public expenditure controls. The RHAs would, as suggested, gradually 'wither on the vine' as they transferred more and more power to the DHAs, eventually becoming regional common service agencies, as in Scotland. Resource allocation would gradually come more and more from the NHS Management Board on a formula basis direct to the DHAs. The DHAs would function with an autonomous FPC responsible for the GPs as independent contractors, but in the same way as in Scotland. The FPC budget would become part of the overall DHA budget.

These evolutionary administrative changes should be accompanied by a steady movement towards an internal market between DHAs. Each DHA, though of course much larger than American health maintenance organizations, would operate within the overall philosophy of health maintenance. They would develop incentives for GPs and others contracted to the FPC to practise in the most cost-effective ways possible. None of these changes can take place rapidly. It will require time to develop the information base, the financial control mechanism and the necessary professional understanding and commitment. What is needed is for the overall framework and objective of unifying the hospital and community services and family practitioner services to be the declared policy of government, and then for the NHS to move towards such a position gradually.

Another problem with the NHS is that it is not in the mainstream of medical research, and this has been identified as a key issue by the House of Lords Select Committee on Science and Technology in their report *Priorities in Medical Research*. They want a national health research authority to operate UK-wide and to be formed as a special health authority within the existing legislation, like the Health Education Authority and the National Health Service Training Authority. This proposal differs from Lord Rothschild's reforms put into operation in 1971 and later abandoned in 1981 under a concordat between the Medical Research Council (MRC) and the DHSS. The MRC would continue with its present arrangement and there would be no withdrawal of MRC money, and also responsibility for primary research would be that of the NHS, not the DHSS. The purpose of the suggested new authority is to enable other bodies involved in medical research to align their activities with NHS needs. The MRC in 1985–6 provided £121.5 million, the DHSS only £17.8 million, charities £110 million, and the pharmaceutical industry £490 million for medical research.

It is always difficult to strike the right balance between targeted, as opposed to basic, research. But analysis in the US has shown that as much as 41% of the essential work for the ten most significant advances in cardiovascular and pulmonory diseases since the early 1940s came from research which was not clinically orientated. Basic research pays off for medicine and that is why the cutbacks in funding levels for the UGC, the MRC and other research councils is so foolishly self-defeating. Equipment needs modernizing and more money is desperately needed.

The pharmaceutical industry offers a good example of the need to integrate NHS policy with industrial and science policy. Only a few years ago the 'knowledge depletion' theory was very much in vogue as a way of explaining why the number of novel medicines being introduced had dropped from fifty a year during the heyday of the pharmacological revolution in the 1950s, to twenty a year at the end of the 1970s. The pharmaceutical industry, it was argued, had largely exploited existing knowledge. But spectacular recent advances in biological science at the cell and sub-cellular level have laid the foundations of a second pharmacological revolution every bit as exciting as the first. The role of pharmacological innovation as a source of improved health should not be exaggerated. It in no way diminishes the urgency of lifestyle changes or alters the priority that should be given to care and support for chronically ill people. But it is very likely that the next decade or two will see really major advances in the prevention and treatment of heart and other circulatory diseases, cancers, diabetes, asthma and possibly conditions like schizophrenia and the dementias.

The key task of government is to create the right market incentives and regulatory framework for the British pharmaceutical industry to deliver medicines profitably and ethically without the NHS being taken for a ride. The industry is justly proud of its record of innovation and export success. Its position as one of the six world market leaders should not be put in jeopardy. But some of its marketing practices are questionable. There is little point in exhorting the industry to act differently. The incentives must be created for the industry to change itself.

The central issue which has emerged from recent reports, including a National Economic Development Office (NEDO) report in 1987 and the House of Lords report on medical research priorities in 1988, is that of patents. The industry has a good case when it argues that the time taken to develop a drug from the laboratory to the clinic has eroded patent lives and tended to reduce incentives. The patent clock starts to tick from the date when the product is marketed. The complexities of modern science, coupled with the time taken for regulatory review, have resulted in effective UK patent lives of less than five years now, compared with fourteen years in 1960. The same trend has been observed worldwide. Both the USA and Japan have responded by legislating to restore the period of pharmaceutical patent to something nearer the theoretical term, but Britain and other European countries have not. Companies which produce truly innovative new medicines must be able to expect a healthy return on their investment.

In order to encourage innovation the patent lives of novel pharmaceutical products should be determined from the date of first marketing rather than the date of filing. We cannot move alone on this because of agreements with our EEC partners, but the government should seek the Europe-wide agreement necessary to enact this measure as speedily as possible.

One consequence of such a change would probably be fewer 'me too' medicines: new products with no significant additional benefits. A shift of marketing strategies from promotion-based protection to patent-based protection would itself discourage many of the questionable marketing techniques now used by many firms to protect their brand names. At the same time there is a need for tougher regulation to keep some of the worst offenders in line.

Better patent protection will go some way to encouraging companies to invest in research on rare diseases. But it has to be recognized that if potential sales are small the incentive to invest will be correspondingly low. The most sensible policy for western governments is to give a clear indication, through their purchasing policies, that they are willing to pay for the cost of successful research into rare diseases through high unit costs for resulting medicines. In the underdeveloped world the problem of market failure is not so easily tackled. The industry's concentration on marketing brand names and not supplying cheaper generic drugs does not deserve to last, but realistically is unlikely to be altered by politicians' pronouncements. It needs to be tackled in part by more effective purchasing policies by many third world countries. But even then the fundamental problem of lack of resources remains. The SDP has previously argued that western governments should respond by funding research contracts to direct the industry into areas of benefit to third world countries. Market failure is arguably at its greatest in the area of vaccines and vaccine research. It is inevitable that third world countries will concentrate on buying existing vaccines as cheaply as possible. But in the absence of patent protection there is little incentive for companies to invest in an area of research which may offer greater human benefits than any other. The nature of the DHSS can be seen from this brief account to be both diverse in its activities and highly political in many of its decision-making areas.

Much has been said since the DHSS was created twenty years ago about whether or not it is too big for one Secretary of State for Social Services to manage. Significantly, that debate usually focuses on managing the acute hospital services and ignores the far more difficult area of community care. This debate is not new and it mostly surfaces when the Secretary of State is felt not to be up to the job. My own experience is that provided that the Secretary of State can delegate, as Barbara Castle successfully did, in order to concentrate on cabinet business and strategic policy questions, the all-embracing coverage of the department has considerable advantages. Admittedly, with a budget of £70 billion, the DHSS accounts for almost half of all government spending, three times as much as the Ministry of Defence. With 1.1 million employees, it is the largest employer in Western Europe. Yet when Health and Social Security were separate, it was hard to justify both ministers having a cabinet position as of right, and the person concerned was never, after Aneurin Bevan, drawn from the ranks of up and coming senior cabinet ministers. It should not be forgotten that Bevan was Minister of Housing at the same time as being Minister of Health. Since Richard Crossman became the first Secretary of State in 1968, the office has been held by persons of varying seniority in the cabinet. More recently it has been held by people who could not command a place in their own right on the all-important Economic Cabinet Committee.

The workload is very heavy, but provided the Secretary of State has three able Ministers of State dealing with social security, health, and community care, there is no need for the Secretary of State to be at the beck and call of all the deputations from the various interest groups, which is one of the most time-consuming of all ministerial activities.

It is when grappling with the development of community care

that the need to marry together social security responsibilities, health responsibilities and local government personal social services responsibilities, is found to be critical. It makes for more effective decision-making if all these responsibilities operate under one roof as long as social security operates separately from taxation. In this structure, the Secretary of State is capable of resolving differences and has considerable flexibility across the department's own budget. In terms of workload for ministers, the more autonomous the NHS in its day-to-day management becomes, the better. The time for a major restructuring of the DHSS will come with the integration of tax and benefits. In this case, much of social security would transfer to the Treasury to operate alongside the semi-autonomous Inland Revenue. In my opinion, unless it is judged opportune to put social security in with the Treasury, it would be better to slim down its executive functions through a national health authority and then to see how a new Minister for Community Care works out within the existing department. When the NHS review is completed, it will need a Secretary of State for Social Services who holds not just the confidence of the Prime Minister, but who can build a base of support for any reforms, not just with those who work in the NHS, but across the party political divide. This requires a figure in the cabinet who has a political future in front of them and some seniority in the cabinet. That is a better way forward than to juggle around now with the machinery of government. Machinery of government changes are usually the refuge of the desperate. If machinery of government changes prove to be the main talking point after the review is complete, it will have failed. What is needed is an evolving structure for the NHS that leaves it with far more executive autonomy and a structure capable of following through many of the worthwhile initiatives already in the system which need time to release their protential. A good place to start looking for constructive ideas is to the various health care systems in other countries.

Chapter 5

LESSONS FROM ABROAD

There are twenty-four countries in the OECD and twenty-four systems. Each of them will tell you that theirs is the best.

OECD health economist

It is not necessary to believe that the whole structure of the National Health Service should be dismantled and replaced by a different system from a foreign blueprint to want to study the health care systems of other countries. Setting our NHS in an international context is useful when examining ways in which it can evolve and improve.

There are as many varieties of health systems as there are countries. But in terms of principles, there are three basic models: national taxation, social insurance and private insurance.

- National taxation is essentially the National Health Service model. It is universal in coverage, and run by the state.
- Social insurance has universal coverage generally within the framework of a state run social security system. It is financed by compulsory employer and individual contributions through non-profit insurance funds.
- Private insurance is not run by state and coverage is not universal. It is financed by individual contributions, employer contributions, or a combination of both.

In all international comparisons what seems to perform well in one country can very rarely be totally transplanted to another. It would be a massive change for us to adopt either social or private insurance and abandon national taxation. But it is sensible and it gives a perspective to our own NHS if we are ready to learn lessons from abroad. Does the NHS, in reality, perform as badly by comparison with some other systems as its detractors claim? Are problems facing the NHS universal and do they confront all health systems? We then discover that what is interesting about other health systems is not how different, but how similar, are the challenges; and that financial worries and cost-containment pressures are a universal problem when facing un-met demand.

The American System

The United States health system is widely regarded by those on the political right as the apotheosis of health provision because of the small degree of government involvement in the system. America spends a higher proportion of its GDP, around 11–12%, on health than any other country in the world. Per capita health spending runs at around £1000 each year, nearly three times the British figure. Yet American public spending on health forms a smaller proportion of total spending on health than any other country. Private spending on health in the United States is 50% higher than public spending. The American system is, therefore, dominated by private insurance coverage, traditionally fee-for-service insurance systems, though Medicare, Medicaid and the growing health-maintenance-organization type of insurance are changing this pattern.

Three quarters of all Americans have private insurance coverage. As the cost of health care suggests, those with the best insurance coverage receive complete coverage and high-standard, even lavish, treatment. For those who are under-insured, or worse, uninsured, it is a different story. They are a significant group but nevertheless a minority. There are around 37 million Americans in this category. For them, ill health brings with it the prospect of either staggering bills for treatment or what amounts to very second-rate treatment in a starkly two-tier system.

Those covered by orthodox private insurance schemes can go to the doctor of their choice. The doctor – effectively an independent supplier unconnected with the insurers – carries out such treatment as is necessary and is reimbursed by the insurer, receiving a fee for each treatment. This can, and frequently does, lead to excessively high health care costs because there is no incentive for doctors to use resources economically and it is to the doctor's advantage to provide more treatment than is strictly necessary.

A flavour of what it is like to live in the US system was given by a journalist, Samira Osman, writing in the *Sunday Times* in April 1988 and describing her pregnancy in Washington DC. She was not insured for obstetric care and since she needed ten months of fully paid up membership to qualify, she had no other option than to pay $6000, at that time about £3700, for pre- and post-natal care. Complications such as a Caesarean section, by which the child would have to be delivered in an emergency by an abdominal operation, would cost extra. An American mother would only qualify for Medicaid if she earned less than $5000.

At one stage in her pregnancy, Samira Osman went to a hospital for tests, which were in fact normal, which cost her $140. She paid a further $80 for pre-natal classes at which she was told that up to 50% of the mothers were likely to have a Caesarean section because it was less risky for the doctor. During her labour she had an epidural injection, costing $350, as an extra, and then at one stage, when the foetal heart rate dropped, it looked as if she might have to have a Caesarean at a further, and unbudgeted, cost of $6000. Despite the anxiety of such an added cost, the heartbeat recovered, the obstetrician with a $60 000 per year malpractice insurance policy felt able to let the baby be born normally and she left hospital with a fit and well daughter and a total bill of $6570 which could well have been $12 570. To describe this experience is to describe a different world for a British mother going into hospital for childbirth.

It is frequently one's personal experiences which affect one's attitude to political issues and this has been the case for me in terms of this type of health care delivery, which I witnessed at first hand some years ago. During my spell as Minister of Health I visited America on a family trip. My eldest child, who was then about four, hit his head and had a deep cut. I rushed him to the nearest hospital. After a heated argument with the doctor to even allow me into the treatment room with him, I stayed while stitches were put in the cut. I remember watching and saying to myself, 'I wouldn't have put in half as many myself.'

Afterwards I went to pay the bill and I was told the charge was $16. I would not have thought twice about that had I not then been told that the breakdown was $10 for the treatment and $6 for the stitches. Inquiring further I was told that the charge was half a dollar per stitch and I thought, 'So that's why he put in twelve stitches.' I would have been prepared to pay any amount to get my son treated, but I realized how the relationship between the patient, or the patient's relatives, and the doctor, changes when payment is on an item-by-service basis. The patient or relative starts to think and say, as I did, 'You know I think he could have managed with fewer stitches there.' The atmosphere changes when there is a cash nexus; it makes for a more equal and less deferential relationship, which is no bad thing, but it also makes for an atmosphere where the patient frequently becomes suspicious of the doctor. This can be very bad for both of them and feeds through into frequent legal cases over malpractice and very high malpractice insurance for the medical profession.

In the US, the cost of rising health expenditure is tending to be met by employers. General increasing health costs also push up the cost of the federal government health care programmes, Medicare and Medicaid. It is this concern about containing costs which has contributed to the growth of health maintenance organizations (HMOs). HMOs contract with a variety of specific doctors and hospitals to provide all health care for a year for their subscribers who pre-pay for their membership. HMOs have been in existence for many years, but it was not until the US Health Maintenance Organization Act of 1973 that they began to expand rapidly. HMOs have fixed budgets. The survival of each HMO, and the income of doctors, depends upon their ability to keep within a budget. Because they contract to provide *all* care, it is imperative for HMOs, if they are to keep within their budget, to keep patients healthy and avoid unnecessary treatment. This financial incentive for proper health screening procedures, and comprehensive preventive care, is a strong advantage of the HMO structure and has led to much praise for, and British interest in, the HMO structure. It is this attitude to health care which is worth trying to bring into the NHS and which has far more relevance than the organizational form which would be very hard to graft on to the NHS.

HMOs can discriminate over who they take on and refuse people on grounds of a poor medical history. But they cannot prudently cut corners to keep their costs down, because if the service is inadequate, the subscribers can enrol in a different HMO the following year. Cutting corners one year can add to costs in another. One disadvantage of HMOs is that they restrict the choice of doctor or hospital open to their members, but in return the members know it is in the HMO's interest to employ good doctors. HMOs are also unable to satisfy the significant number who are termed 'worried well', demanding frequent and sophisticated treatment which is usually not medically necessary. They operate most economically for the healthy, working population. As an addition to the American system rather than a substitute for it, they will continue to prosper. But if they were expected to cover all groups, then not only would subscriptions have to rise, but the role of the federal and state governments in underwriting their costs could increase, getting ever closer to a National Health Service. That may be how US health care will evolve with an ever increasing role for the state. Certainly that is the direction where it is currently pointing.

The American system fails what in Britain is a basic test of a health system, namely over the absence of universal coverage. Although the coverage of Medicare and Medicaid, and with that the cost, has risen quite sharply since the 1960s, there remain a great many Americans who are not adequately provided for. There are many people who cannot easily afford to join an HMO or a health insurance scheme who are not old enough for Medicare, and not poor enough for Medicaid. Although there is a federal poverty line set at $12 000 (£6500) per annum, this is subject to state variations so that probably no more than half those who are poor by federal standards actually receive aid. Such people would almost always receive emergency treatment, and then in all probability – if they have assets over about £1600 – be charged part of the cost. If, however, they are ill but not critically or terminally so, they will find it hard to get treatment anywhere.

There are around 18 million mainly blue-collar and self-employed people who do not receive HMO or insurance cover through their employers. They have to pay the full cost of insurance coverage which is very expensive and rarely comprehensive. There are around 2.5 million American families that face medical bills, over and above the cost of any insurance premiums, of more than $3000 each year. The cost of health insurance is pushed still higher by the hidden addition of the cost of the doctors' own insurance against negligence claims. This type of claim has reached epidemic proportions and all but driven out of the health system a number of groups of professionals, notably nurse–midwives.

A further problem with the system is the scope of insurance coverage. A great many Americans – particularly older people – have found that both HMOs and health insurance companies will either refuse to accept them because they are too high-risk, or will not provide coverage for those illnesses which they are likely to contract. This is almost diametrically opposite to the NHS principle of health care bing provided on the basis of need. It excludes many from the network of HMOs and insurance companies which give good health care to those fortunate enough to have full coverage.

The American health care system costs twice as much as the NHS and for most Americans provides very high quality health care in cleaner, newer, better-equipped hospitals and medical centres than will be found in Britain or most other countries. Yet the American system is also one in which people can suffer because they are not adequately protected against illness, pain and discomfort and more than a tenth of the population have no insurance cover at all.

The Canadian System

The Canadian health system makes an interesting case history. Canada has had to face up to the problems of burgeoning health costs and has done so within a comprehensive and universal health care system in which patients' rights and choices are treated with respect.

By contrast to the United States, in Canada there is now a broad acceptance of a major federal governmental role in orientating the organization of provincial health services. This has resulted in the gradual move from a mixed public and private insurance system to a universal compulsory public insurance system. The previous system excluded a significant proportion of the population, particularly those in most need, and could not assure coverage of very large costs. The effective monopolization of the payment process, by the introduction of a full universal public insurance system, which was completed in 1971, has enabled much more effective control on expenditure while entrenching the principle that the whole population is covered for all essential services. The change between 1968 and 1971 that brought about the comprehensive universal health insurance system was as much about concern for rising costs as any concern to improve the scope and standards of social services. The effect has been the building of a system which is not far from being a National Health Service but one in which hospitals are largely independently or locally owned.

Medical services are provided primarily by private doctors reimbursed on a fee-for-service basis. Acute care hospitals are generally owned by municipalities, voluntary societies or universities and run by boards of trustees. There is little public intervention in the actual delivery of health care. Provincial governments only direct the decisions of hospitals in as much as they determine which general activities will be reimbursed.

The development of a universal public insurance system has also led to a highly developed strategy of long-range health planning. The 1974 report by a former Minister of Health and Welfare, Marc Lalonde, *A New Perspective on the Health of Canadians*, argued that there were four elements to consider in determining health policy: human biology, environment, lifestyle and health care organization. The report concluded that too much emphasis was generally placed on tinkering with the mechanisms of health care organization and that human biology, environment and lifestyle should be raised 'to a level of categorical importance equal to that of health care organization so that all our avenues of improved health are pursued with equal vigour'.[1] This approach encouraged health planners, both federally and in the provinces, to assess their health policy and expenditure on a general principle of risk-factor reduction and to place greater emphasis on preventive medicine. It stimulated me when Minister of Health to produce, in 1975, for the first time a publication for discussion by the DHSS on preventive medicine, *Prevention and Health: Everyone's Business*, and this did something to provoke a public debate and parliamentary scrutiny of our preventive health priorities.

Canada's health system is intended to meet the health needs of all through a system which is financed by general taxation or compulsory health insurance premiums. Since 1966 the Canadian federal government has been responsible for working with provincial governments to maintain a comprehensive health plan encompassing doctor's service, acute hospital care, laboratory and radiology services. Federal government defines the basic principles of the system but the provinces have the responsibility of their actual local policy. This apparent freedom does allow for variations among the different provinces, but all must and do meet certain federal criteria in order to receive federal assistance. These criteria include accessibility, universality, and comprehensive coverage.

Prior to 1977 the federal government paid 50% of all costs incurred by the province. In 1977, in part as a response to the Lalonde report, the Federal–Provincial Fiscal Arrangement and Established Programs Finance Act was enacted. This enabled much greater flexibility and more effective autonomous planning by basing the federal contribution to provincial health care on a three-year lump sum calculated from a three-year moving average of GNP and a per capita cash payment. The federal resources were no longer limited specifically to hospital and medical services, and provinces were able to invest in extended health care programmes such as drug-rehabilitation centres, nursing homes, and community care programmes. Following the 1977 Act, resources were allocated in advance of the year, after rigorous scrutiny of costs, and on the basis that hospitals must stay within budget. Overspending is the problem of the hospitals. Hospitals which underspend can spend the surplus on new buildings or equipment. This positive incentive to financial self-discipline is a great advance on current NHS procedures.

The provision of an autonomous health fund has profound lessons for us in the UK: in Canada it has given health planners greater stability and the capacity to consider health problems in the round, linking hospital and community care.

The Canadian health system has proved consistently popular with its consumers, although attracting some criticism from the Canadian Medical Association. Universal public insurance has brought firmer cost control, so that health spending now absorbs a relatively stable proportion of national income, at a level which by international standards is fairly high. The standard of patient care is regarded as excellent. The Canadian system recognizes and treats the patient as a 'customer' with rights and choices. Overall, Canada manages to provide universal care which is frequently likened to 'private patient care' in Britain. Canada achieves the advantages of a unified system and those of national strategic direction while also gaining the benefit of decentralized application.

Some doctors and hospitals, as they will always do, argue that the system is under-funded, resulting in outdated equipment, growing waiting lists for non-urgent surgery and overcrowded hospitals. The principal focus of protest on the part of doctors, however, has been the practice of 'extra billing'. This has been a means by which doctors can circumvent the constraints of the reimbursement system in order to enhance their income. The practice grew throughout the 1970s and, in some provinces, led to the beginnings of a two-tier system whereby preferential treatment was available to patients who could afford to pay an extra charge to the doctor. In 1984 Canadians paid $70 million to physicians who 'extra bill'. The federal government sought to abolish the practice by establishing financial disincentives for provinces which allow extra billing and then by the passage of the Canada Health Act, 1984. This Act successfully curbed the great majority of extra billing, although not without a rearguard action by doctors. A twenty-five-day strike by doctors in Ontario failed to deter the prohibition of extra billing, an act described by the Ontario Medical Association as 'a mortal attack on our professional freedom'.[2]

One of the problems which Canada uniquely faces is having a long open border with the United States, where they compete not only against a different system, but one in which doctors are highly paid and health spending is particularly high.

The Japanese System

Japan is an intriguing country which has combined vigorous economic growth with the lowest expenditure on health, as a proportion of its not inconsiderable GDP, of any OECD country. Throughout the 1960s Japan enjoyed a very high level of prosperity. The promotion of health and investment in welfare were, however, not high priorities. Yet as high economic growth continued, the importance of a qualitative improvement in people's lives, rather than just accumulating material possessions, took root and national policy began to place greater importance on welfare. In 1973 the Japanese government declared the first 'welfare year' and implemented a free health care cost programme for the elderly. In 1961 a compulsory health insurance scheme had been introduced giving all Japanese citizens coverage under health insurance schemes, either on the basis of employment status or residence. By 1980, 99.3% of the total population was covered by these insurance schemes, and the remaining 0.7% was covered by the statutory medical assistance programme, or by special programmes for particular categories such as mental illness.

Patients have the right to go direct to a hospital or to the clinic of their choice. Full reimbursement of any cost incurred is granted through the insurance system, including examination, treatment and medication. Those who are covered by insurance only as dependants of insured people are responsible for 30% of their costs, although all costs over about £100 are subsidized. The elderly are charged a proportion of their treatment costs, with a growing emphasis on the need to charge for residence in general hospital beds.

There are two types of insurance available to the Japanese: insurance provided by government, and private insurance through health insurance societies. Any company employing more than three hundred people can, with the consent of both the Ministry for Health and Welfare and of at least half the workforce, establish a health insurance society. The societies are incorporated bodies and are responsible for their own management. They may either provide their own facilities and medical benefits in kind, or simply reimburse actual costs. In 1980 there were 1670 health insurance societies covering more than 11 million members and 16 million dependants. Under both society and government insurance the employer is required to pay a certain amount for each employee and, in addition, to deduct automatically a proportion of the employee's pay which is taken by government to support health care. There is a financial incentive to the employee to join a health insurance society because the deduction made for health care from wages is lower. Additional administrative expenses are absorbed by the national Treasury.

Those Japanese who are not covered through their place of work are covered on the basis of residence. More than 16 million households and 45 million individuals receive health coverage in this way. The providers under this system include cities, towns and villages, although national health societies do exist.

The Japanese health insurance system has led to a rapid and significant growth in demand on the health services which is exacerbated by the familiar worldwide demographic pressure of a rapidly ageing population. By the 1980s the Japanese government had become very concerned with attempting to contain demand for health care services, which they feared was increasing at such a rate as to be too great a burden on the economy. In 1983 and 1985 the Japanese government legislated to contain costs within the health system, and to try to contain demand – principally by increasing charges.

In Japan, health care costs continue to increase faster than GNP. Their health economists have focused on charging the elderly population who represent, as in most health systems, a disproportionately high part of health care costs. By increasing health charges on the elderly, they are attempting to hold the rate of increase in spending on health care to the rate of growth of the economy as a whole. The furore in Britain would be considerable if our government were to advocate either consciously limiting the supply of health care to old people, or charging them to recover full costs. Though logical, it is not a humane response to the problems of an ageing population. It takes no account of the responsibility that the younger generation have for the older generation. Nevertheless, it illustrates the different ethics of health policy which prevail in different countries. It does provide, however, a warning to us in Britain about shifting the burden for financing health care on to the working population and excluding a contribution from the elderly, which would be the effect of funding the NHS from the present national insurance contribution system as described in Chapter 10, Paying for the NHS.

The French System

One of the first acts of the post-war provisional government of France under de Gaulle was the establishment of 'Les Ordonnances de la Sécurité Sociale'. 'La Sécu', as it is now popularly known, comprised a mandatory health insurance scheme providing comprehensive national health coverage with equal benefits for all. This was to be the French equivalent to the British Beveridge welfare state model.

In France, insurance is compulsory and social security pays, usually, 70% of the cost of care. The cost of this is met from a national-insurance-type system of deductions in the workplace: 5.9% of pay for employees, 12.6% for employers. The remaining 30% is topped up by non-profit insurance companies – 'mutuelles' – whose coverage usually costs another 2.5% of salary. Orthodox private insurance is also available. Social security for those defined as poor, although this definition is pretty strict, covers all their costs, and for a number of defined illnesses, including cancer, care is free.

French hospitals, 70% of which are publicly owned and 30% privately owned, levy a nominal bed and breakfast charge. In addition patients are in theory expected to pay 20% of their hospital expenses. In practice, such payment is rare because most hospital stays are either exempted under the schedule of 24 exempt diseases, or exceed a person's ability to pay. There is no charge for either maternity or psychiatric beds. Prescription costs are met up to 70%, or 40% for a list of specific non-vital drugs. This differential prescription charge is an interesting concept that could be examined for the UK.

To those used to the NHS and a straightforward health care delivery system, this array of exemptions and reimbursement scales seems excessively complex. The French would argue, however, that it is a natural development of a system where there is genuine cooperation between private and public sectors, and a genuine choice for patients.

The French system is made both more complex and probably less efficient by the elevation of consumer choice to be an overriding principle in the patient's relationship to doctors, though it is good to see patients' interests being placed first. They can choose a specialist or doctor according to what they think is wrong with them. If they are dissatisfied with the diagnosis or treatment they go to a different doctor. Health economists point out that this system leads to a very costly use of scarce skills. Patients may – and frequently do – consult a number of different doctors for the same complaint. It also leads to a generally patchy system of medical records which inevitably, at times, impairs the speed and accuracy of both diagnosis and treatment. It can result in inefficient duplication of resources while bringing little tangible benefit to the patient.

The strict French system for eligibility to free treatment also has some adverse effects. The safety net sometimes fails to catch those who cannot afford to pay a proportion of their treatment or who do not have, or cannot afford, the top-up insurance available to most through the mutuelles. This means that those who do slip through the safety net often wait to seek treatment until they are ill enough to warrant hospital care and to receive full reimbursement.

There are clear drawbacks to the French multi-provider system. Planning is difficult. Administrative costs are very high. Supply at times outstrips demand so that equipment lies idle. It is furthermore a very costly system. France spends 9.4% of its GDP on health, more than any other Western European country, 60% more than Britain. A consequence of this is that the French health system boasts an impressive range of modern facilities.

Much of its high level of spending, however, is not efficiently spent or economically invested. Simmering in the background for a number of years has been concern about how to control health care costs and establish a constant target for health spending as a proportion of GDP.

What is admirable in the French system, however, is its consumer orientation and the marked absence of ideological preoccupation with the boundaries between public and private medical practice. The French view that public and private systems are complementary allows public and private hospitals together to combine to provide a sort of national health grid. We in Britain can learn from this if we can lose some of our ideological prejudices. Over 300 private hospitals are fully integrated into the French system. Patients can opt to go to these private hospitals in preference to a public hospital. They can if they wish also pay a fairly low extra charge to see a consultant of their choice, or to occupy a private room.

In part the removal of political controversy from the divide between the public and private sectors in France is possible because hospital waiting lists are not such an endemic feature as they are of the British system. Equally, however, the semi-integration of the private sector into the state system has itself contributed to reductions in waiting times. The contrast is marked. In the early 1960s the French government sought to abolish pay-beds in public hospitals, just as the 1974–9 Labour government tried to do in Britain. As in Britain, it was a policy which did not work. Now as many as 15% of beds in any ward of a French public hospital can be private. There are lessons here for us in Britain, but only if we are ready and able to make a substantial reduction in our NHS waiting lists.

The West German System

The West German health system is worthy of careful examination if only because it faces precisely the opposite problem to the British NHS. The health service suffers not from shortages and waiting lists, but from over-supply. Normally we find when looking at Germany much to admire. Yet a German official told a British journalist, Graham Turner, writing for the *Daily Mail*, 'I've a feeling you can't learn much from us. We can no longer go on financing the rising cost of our health system. The way our hospitals are funded, for example, is the most stupid you can possibly imagine.'[3]

Medical care in Germany is financed basically through the statutory health insurance system which covers 90% of the population. There are 1200 public insurance schemes mainly covering groups of employees. Employees earning less than about DM54 000 (£18 000) per annum are obliged to join such schemes. This applies to some 55% of the population. They pay, on average, about 6.3% of their salaries to cover insurance for themselves and any family not otherwise covered. The employer has to contribute a similar amount.

The largest of the public insurance schemes is the Allgemeine Ortskrankenkasse (AOK) – a state organization obligated to insure people who are not part of an employee group insurance scheme, or who otherwise cannot obtain insurance. This scheme not surprisingly attracts a very high proportion of unemployed and poor people. This illustrates a fundamental flaw in a health insurance system with many different insurers. An insurer of last resort, like the AOK, is responsible for a large proportion of high-risk groups which push up insurance premiums accordingly. The most efficient, and also the most equitable, form of insurance is a universal system which spreads risk as evenly as possible and therefore minimizes average premiums and their variability. A system with a multiplicity of insurance schemes, even if the majority are public, inevitably leads to an uneven spread of risk and distortions to the level of premiums.

In addition to the public insurance system, 7.5% of the population belong to private health insurance schemes; 6.7% of those covered by the statutory system have additional private insurance so that they can, for example, have a choice of a doctor in hospital, or a single room. Around 0.3% of the population, the very rich, have no insurance coverage.

The statutory insurance system gives full coverage of medical care. State employees are reimbursed between 50% and 70% of the cost of treatment; the overwhelming majority have private insurance cover as well to cover them for the remainder. Each of the various public insurance schemes is self-governed and organized at both state and federal level. All doctors and dentists who work within the statutory system have to belong to an organization of physicians and dentists which negotiates details of health provision with the organization covering all the public insurance schemes. In general the insurance schemes provide extraordinarily comprehensive care – including provision in some cases for convalescence in spa towns. The only common complaint from consumers about the service they receive has been related to the failure of the government – despite legislation – to eliminate the incidence of separate areas within hospitals and medical centres for private patients.

The extent of over-supply within the German system is causing alarm. According to the federal government's own figures, West Germany has 50 000 too many hospital beds; 1147 beds per 100 000 of the population compared with 614 per 100 000 in Britain. There are 165 000 doctors in West Germany, 270 per 100 000. By contrast there are 160 doctors (NHS and private) per 100 000 of the population in Britain. These totals, as the federal government plaintively puts it, 'keep rising'. There is serious concern that over-supply is leading to the health service running short of money.

The spending of the statutory health insurance schemes has risen sharply due to more comprehensive and advanced medical care, and longer life expectancy. In 1960 spending on these schemes amounted to DM9.5 billion. In 1987 it stood at DM108 billion, DM8 billion more than revenue from contributions. This expenditure requires contributions averaging 12.6% of the gross earnings of those insured. Schemes such as the AOK with a large number of bad risks frequently have to levy up to 14%. Because the contributions are deductions at source, and are employment-related in the vast majority of cases, the schemes have the same disadvantage as national insurance contributions in Britain in terms of their impact as a payroll tax deterring companies from taking on more staff, and reducing their investment capacity.

The concern in Germany at high health spending, which has been growing over a number of years, has now led to the introduction in 1988 of reforms by the government. The proposed structure will guarantee health care for all, but it introduces the provision that the insurance schemes must pay only what is medically necessary. More extensive treatment, including expensive dental work which accounts for the single largest growth area in health spending since 1960, and hospital treatment not considered 'absolutely essential', must be paid for by the patient.

The government is also introducing a series of transitional charges which will apply 'until the expenditure and revenue of the statutory health insurance schemes are once again in balance'.[4] These transitional charges include 20% of prescription costs, 40% of cost of medical aids, a flat-rate grant only for hearing aids, and a restriction that only the cost of lenses for spectacles, not the frames, will be met. Attempts are also being made to reduce future health costs by investing in a programme of preventive medicine and health education. Financial incentives have been proposed by charging a smaller proportion of medical expenses to those going for regular medical check-ups.

The government hopes, by these changes, to save some DM14 billion a year. Half of this will go back to the insured through a 1% reduction in contributions. The other DM7 billion is earmarked for an area of health policy which we in Britain would do well to consider as we try to make a reality of community care. Relatives who care for severely handicapped people in their homes will in future be able to take an extra four weeks' holiday a year on top of their normal entitlement at the expense of the statutory health insurance schemes. They will also be able to gain some respite leave by the entitlement to have a nurse relieve them for one hour each day.

From this brief comparison of health care systems it is possible to conclude that there is no other comparable health care system which spends less than the NHS. There is no health care system which appears to be convincingly more cost-effective. If the NHS had more financial resources it is reasonable to conclude that much of the present consumer dissatisfaction would cease. It is impossible to put a figure with any certainty on what is needed but it is hard to avoid the conclusion that the UK should be aiming to provide for a step-like increase in health spending to raise it to 7–7.5% of GDP in a few years. From this higher base, health care costs would rise, taking a growing proportion of GDP, as they have in Britain and in other countries.

It is not possible to conclude from these comparative studies that the NHS is the only defensible system, nor even necessarily the best, but it is a system that can be defended on economic, not just on ethical, grounds.

> Allowing doctors, broadly speaking, to determine treatment is not professional elitism. It results from a recognition that in this area there will always be a degree of consumer ignorance.

> The family doctor as an honest broker, not allowing patient access to consultants, acts as a check on professional exploitation which is an undoubted problem in certain other countries.

> A mostly salaried service, with only a small claim-by-service element, reduces what economists call 'third party payment incentives' to provide more than is needed.

> Running health care mainly out of general taxation and predominantly free at the point of use avoids the gaps which are a feature of private insurance and makes it less likely that a two-tier system will emerge.

> The inevitable rationing of health care is broadly fair in the NHS in terms of both patients and type of treatment.

> The tendency of the British system to fail to meet demand is a reflection on national decision-making remote from consumer needs and unable to ensure cost-effective provision.

> The national character of the NHS effectively gives the district health authority a splendid excuse to under-perform – for everyone can blame everyone else.

There are many important lessons to learn from studying the health care systems of other countries. By far the most important is that the absence of an external market in health does lead to inefficiency and unfilled demand, so that there is a substantial case for creating an internal market within the NHS.

Chapter 6

A MARKET IN HEALTH

Physicians of the Utmost Fame
Were called at once; but when they came
They answered, as they took their fees,
'There is no cure for this disease.'

Hilaire Belloc, *Cautionary Tales*

Will the economic arguments for introducing market forces into health care, little different from those for introducing market forces in other areas of day-to-day living, distort a health care system based on matching scarce resources to health needs? Competition brings more customer and consumer choice and this variety gives a more efficient allocation of resources than through a centrally directed bureaucratic system; but unless the market allocation of resources is tempered by medical and social criteria, the distortion will be socially unacceptable. For that reason, none of the democratic industrialized countries operates a free market health care system.

Until recently, the argument for a market in health care in Britain was polarized between those who advocated a system in which individuals were enabled to buy their own health care, and those who believed in the collectivist allocation of scarce health resources by the state. A pure market health service lets the consumer decide; a pure collectivist health service lets the producer decide. In reality no pure system exists. The NHS is not a pure collectivist system, but not surprisingly, many doctors and nurses as producers tend to be quite comfortable within what is a broadly collectivist health service. In the NHS they are able to allocate their scarce skills as they feel medical need demands. The problem with this pattern of distributing health care is that it tends to be paternalistic and very unresponsive to patient wishes. Patients as consumers are starting to feel less patient as they either wait for treatment or find themselves directed as to where to go for treatment at a time when in most other areas their choices are becoming wider and freer.

The recent advocacy of an internal market within the NHS is changing the nature of the debate and arousing considerable interest, primarily because it could bring the beneficial effects of competition and choice without challenging the ethical basis of the NHS which dictates that care is based on health need, not on the capacity to pay. An ideal NHS would be one which balances consumer and producer sovereignty and will never allow either to dominate the other. Achieving that degree of pluralism sufficient to give maximum individual choice without distorting the distribution of scarce resources on the basis of medical need requires us to know far more about the economics of the NHS than we presently do.

Slowly the economics of health care is making an impact, so that there is a growing consensus behind the present emphasis on resource management. The experimental resource management initiative which started in 1986 in six hospitals and which is being monitored jointly by the NHS Management Board and the Joint Consultants Committee will add to everyone's knowledge. It is hoped that it will be able to show measurable improvements in patient care, provide clinicians with information to identify waste and inefficiency, and expose for debate the health care consequences of financial decisions. In health, as in education, the pressure for greater consumer choice should not become the monopoly of Conservatives and the political right. A truly redistributive left would focus on choice as a liberating influence of far more value to the poor because they have much less experience of choice than the rich.

It is often insufficiently appreciated, in the arguments about the desirability or otherwise of introducing a market into our health service, how much the British health care system benefits already from not being purely collectivist. It is not just that the existence of a private health service alongside the NHS has always provided an alternative choice for those who can afford it, but that it provides a point of comparison which is of benefit to all. Built into the NHS are numerous mechanisms which ensure it has never been, nor could easily become, a pure collectivist system. The NHS has also demonstrated a fertile adaptive capacity throughout its forty years and it is interesting to see how it is still adapting. It was Aneurin Bevan who accepted not only that private practice should not be banned by law, but that since it would exist, there were some advantages in it existing co-located with the NHS. As a consequence, pay-beds and private consulting rooms were deliberately allowed within NHS hospitals. Doctors were granted contracts with the NHS which provided for them to practise privately under what was then called a maximum part-time contract. They were paid nine elevenths of a wholetimer's salary, but expected to devote substantially the whole of their time to the NHS. It was Aneurin Bevan too who recognized that privacy was something patients could pay for in the NHS without distorting its values. Amenity beds have always allowed NHS patients to purchase a single room, on the strict understanding that this was not a mechanism for purchasing priority treatment either in jumping a waiting list or in obliging a consultant to treat personally any patient in an amenity bed. The GP's independent contractor status has been another way in which the NHS, from its inception, established a market-orientated independent contractor relationship. Theoretically at least, the unpopular family doctor would have a small list and therefore earn less than a popular colleague with a larger list.

A controversial question has been whether to charge the patient for drugs, both as a source of revenue, and as an economic disincentive to patients regarding drugs as a necessary and automatic accompaniment of any visit to a doctor. Prescription charges were reluctantly accepted as probably necessary in principle by Aneurin Bevan when the Chancellor, Stafford Cripps, imposed financial constraints on the cabinet in 1950. Admittedly, Bevan always hoped that prescription charges would never have to be implemented, but there were wider political issues when he fought Hugh Gaitskell, the new Chancellor, who tried to introduce them in 1951. By the time Bevan resigned from the cabinet he had wisely sought to extend his area of disagreement from the narrow issue of prescription charges to include the costs of the rearmament programme for the Korean War. In this way, Bevan ensured that he took with him out of the Labour government both Harold Wilson and John Freeman, since for them prescription charges were an important emotional issue within the Labour Party, but a secondary matter against the costs of rearmament.

It has also always been accepted within the NHS that private medicine could purchase, at cost, services from the NHS, and that this commercial traffic could go both ways. Revenue from such charging has been greatly increased in recent years, but it is not introducing a new principle. Hospitals have allowed – often for a peppercorn rent – flowers and food to be sold on NHS premises and banking facilities have been available. What is new is the extent to which, in the last few years, all of these commercial activities and market-orientated features have been built on and expanded in the desperate search to increase health funds. In a sense, however, this is no more than following a pattern previously seen in the growing number of commercial franchises on railway stations and other public premises.

The NHS has fortunately, therefore, never been a 'pure' model of a collectivist health service. There has been a public/private mix from the start and indeed that mix and the flexibility within that mix has undoubtedly helped to give the NHS its relative political stability. There is no question that highly specialized consultant surgeons, capable of earning very substantial incomes in the private sector, would never have been kept predominantly within the NHS if there had not been a system of merit or distinction awards.

The 12 000 hospital medical and dental staff will have in 1988 a basic salary of £27 500 to £35 000. In addition, the annual values of distinction and meritorious service awards for consultants will mean that 192 consultants have A-plus awards of £29 550 to £33 720; 692 consultants have A awards of £22 750 to £24 850; 1679 consultants have B awards of £13 000 to £14 200; and 3902 consultants have C awards of £5790 to £6260.

The merit awards ensure a standard of living for NHS consultants which, while not matching what many might earn if they worked solely in private practice, has nevertheless provided them with a sizeable incentive to continue within the NHS, at least for the majority of their professional activity. The assessment of which doctors should be rewarded is made by the profession and this has been done fairly, though somewhat conventionally and with too great a tendency to reward seniority. Publishing the awards has been strongly resisted on the exaggerated ground that it would lead to patients demanding to be referred by their GPs only to those consultants who hold awards – another example of how the profession restricts competitive pressures. The awards would benefit not just from greater public scrutiny but greater involvement of health service managers, and should be renewable as the Doctors' Review Body has suggested and as has been already referred to in Chapter 2, The Medical Profession.

A flexible and pragmatic approach to the private sector in Britain has been maintained despite many political pressures to expand it or to curtail it. An interesting development illustrating this very flexibility is that, from the passing of the Abortion Act in 1967, the percentage of abortions performed on UK residents in the NHS actually dropped from 69% to 51% in 1987. Private clinics and nursing homes dealt with an increasing number of abortions as the total number of abortions rose in that period from just over 37 000 to nearly 63 000 in 1987. This way of meeting demand was pursued with the cooperation of Labour as well as Conservative governments. Some of the private clinics were run by charitable organizations set up deliberately to compensate for the lack of provision in the NHS, either because of inadequate facilities or because NHS consultants in that particular area objected to the terms of the Act and continued to adopt a restrictive attitude to requests for abortions. Another major expansion of the private sector in health care has been the growth of private homes for the elderly and to a lesser extent for the mentally ill and handicapped as the trend to phase out the large psychiatric and mental handicap hospitals gathered momentum. Again, this growth occurred under both Labour and Conservative governments. The very important questions which are raised by the risk that this government is about to restrict elderly patients' virtually open access to these homes is discussed in Chapter 8, Community Care.

The Labour Party's traditional fear of the private sector was that its growth would threaten the NHS. In fact, the number of patients treated in pay-beds only increased from 78 000 in 1950 to 113 000 by 1974 – a rate of increase no greater than the growth in the overall number of NHS patients treated. Yet from the start, many activists in the Labour Party had been unhappy with Aneurin Bevan's initial compromise of allowing private beds in NHS hospitals. Had it not been for the threatened strike action by GPs in 1964, the resolution of which had to be the highest priority, curbing private medicine would have been forced on to the agenda of the 1964 Labour government, particularly when it was returned with a large majority in 1966. The then Health Minister, Kenneth Robinson, was, however, a practical, non-ideological politician who had specialized in health matters and so was well aware that a confrontation with the doctors over the role of private medicine was the last thing the NHS needed.

When Labour returned to government in 1974, the situation was very different. The new Secretary of State for Social Services, Barbara Castle, was a charismatic, ideological politician, very conscious of her role on the National Executive of the Labour Party and keen to restore her credibility with the trade unions, which she had badly damaged when Secretary of State for Employment over her 1968 trade union reform package, 'In Place of Strife'. To Barbara Castle, fulfilling Labour's manifesto pledge to phase out pay-beds from the NHS was almost a sacred mission, redressing the error which her hero, Aneurin Bevan, had made in the original legislation. She also knew, as did I – the newly appointed Health Minister – that the manifesto commitment to the phasing out of pay-beds was itself a compromise reluctantly accepted by the health service unions in place of a commitment to an all-out legislative ban on private practice. I felt that the policy of phasing out pay-beds, as distinct from the abolition of private medicine, was necessary, given the public resentment of queue jumping within an NHS hospital, although I was well aware that the medical profession would fight it tooth and nail. It had been becoming harder and harder to justify a situation where private patients were able to jump the queue in NHS hospitals. Whereas few minded if in private hospitals people were treated more rapidly than in NHS hospitals, I hoped that provided pay-beds were only gradually phased out, while at the same time consultants were granted a new contract with extra money, we might get away without serious disruption. That proved too optimistic an assumption, mainly because the medical profession wanted to believe that what Barbara Castle was really about was abolishing private medicine. The BMA argued that phasing out pay-beds was the thin end of the wedge: part of a grand strategy to end private medicine. They were given some justification for that belief by Barbara Castle's determination that private beds should go without much time for private facilities to be built to replace those lost from within the NHS. She compounded their belief by her zeal to introduce a licensing arrangement to control the building of new facilities for private medicine, or the adaptation of existing ones. Given their attitudes, many Labour-controlled local authorities were clearly going to put all possible political barriers in the way of any planning applications for private hospitals.

The medical profession's fears were then quite suddenly whipped up to a feverish pitch when, in July 1974, the whole pay-bed issue broke into the public's consciousness. Splash headlines about 'Granny', 'Ma' or 'Mrs' Brookestone's strike against private patients in Charing Cross Hospital, depending on which newspaper one read, inflamed the whole issue. One of the penalties of the highly centralized NHS with a controversial cabinet minister at its head is that relatively minor issues can suddenly capture public concern and then engulf ministers. A small section of NUPE in Charing Cross Hospital was demanding that the privileges of the private fifteenth floor should be shared by NHS patients so as to shorten waiting lists, and were withholding their services to these patients. The local area health authority had almost agreed on a compromise but then the local consultants, stiffened by the BMA, decided to make this issue into one of major principle and determined that they would continue to insist on their legal right to admit up to a predetermined number of private beds.

The whole episode is graphically described in *The Castle Diaries*

1974–76. It is a vignette of history, a sharp reminder of how very different attitudes were in the 1970s compared to the 1980s. Then we were in the last throes of the corporatist state in which trade union leaders, whether NUPE or the BMA, expected to bargain directly with ministers. It was the time of beer and sandwiches at Number 10. It was part of a different era which ended with the 'Winter of Discontent' in 1979 and the defeat of the Labour government. Talks, with Barbara Castle actively involved, went on at the DHSS offices at the Elephant and Castle well into the early hours of the morning. They included not just the local management and unions, but the British Medical Association and the general secretaries of NUPE and COHSE, the latter at one stage having to be dragged from his caravan, in his pyjamas in the middle of the night, outside into the pouring rain, to speak to Barbara Castle from a public telephone box.

Eventually a complicated formula was arrived at whereby the private floor would become a mixed ward. Unfortunately, no one had yet squared Mrs Brookstone. Barbara Castle vividly described what then happened. 'She was no fool and soon realized that they hadn't got the magic formula on which they had pinned their hopes: the release of twenty private beds for the NHS. "All we have got is one for one," she complained. "Yes, Brooky," explained one of the consultants – now free from the shadow of the BMA to renew his normal friendly relations with Ma B. and her members – "but you know that the private floor is always under-occupied. In future these beds will not be kept empty. When we move a private patient to a specialized unit, as we do frequently, we will move an NHS patient immediately into the empty bed".'[1]

What a farce it was. Yet behind that episode was a serious issue, a struggle between NUPE and the BMA for the power to influence the Secretary of State. The consequences were particularly damaging. Instead of quietly phasing out pay-beds, the issue had suddenly acquired a very high public profile and, what was worse, we had been forced to bring forward the complicated negotiations over the consultants' contract. That resulted in an explosive mix and a confrontation with the BMA at the end of the year over the terms of their contract. Barbara Castle was accused of making a 'take it or leave it' offer which was, in effect, no more than a cabinet decision on what the government was prepared to pay out. Hospital consultants then started to work to rule, nominally because of their anger over the breakdown of the contract negotiations. In reality the pay-beds issue was the spark that ignited the profession. Waiting lists rose, NHS morale plummeted, the junior hospital doctors demanded payment for overtime, at one stage even the GPs were on the point of taking action.

Eventually the pay-beds issue was resolved by private talks using Lord Goodman as an intermediary between Mr Grabham, an NHS consultant surgeon negotiating for the BMA, and Barbara Castle for the government. Much of this took place in Arnold Goodman's flat, where he and I met in the hall to relay the respective positions of our principals. It ended with what probably I alone – because of my West Country background – always think of as the 'Cullompton Compromise'. Cullompton is a small market town in Devon where Arnold Goodman had served during the war and which he used to illustrate the financial problem facing a mythical consultant with no private hospital in existence and faced by the sudden withdrawal of pay-beds from the local NHS hospital. The solution was an independent Health Service Board to supervise the phasing out of pay-beds. The phasing out was to operate at a pace to be determined only by the board, and they had to take into account the availability of alternative private provision. It was not a bad compromise given the circumstances. The Health Service Board, by 1 January 1979, had reduced the number of pay-beds to 2819 in Great Britain compared to 4444 in 1976, the first thousand revocations of pay-beds being authorized because of under-usage. The board was then wound up by the incoming Conservative government in 1980; pay-beds were encouraged.

It was, by any standard, a fruitless dispute. It deeply damaged the NHS for a negligible return. Politicians should learn from their mistakes and certainly I would never dream of embarking on a similar exercise. What is perhaps more important, I believe the NHS unions have also realized that further controversy over pay-beds within the NHS is futile. The Royal Commission on the NHS was right to conclude, in 1979, that 'from the point of view of the NHS the main importance of pay-beds lies in the passions aroused and the consequential dislocation of work which then occurs'. It is in everyone's interests that these passions appear to have subsided. If only we could reduce waiting lists, and therefore the instances of 'queue jumping', the existence of pay-beds would be of little concern and the original Bevan compromise would continue to be acceptable.

There are signs that the issue of pay-beds is now seen, even within the Labour Party, to be a damaging irrelevance to the really dangerous development of a two-tier health service: a well-endowed private sector and a 'poor relation' public sector for those who cannot afford private insurance. The health unions know that while long waiting lists exist in the NHS, more people will 'go private', including trade unions, as the way of ensuring that they do not wait for non-urgent elective surgery. It is on the eradication of waiting lists that the opponents of private medicine should concentrate.

In 1988, there were 90 000 private sector beds outside the NHS, almost 10 000 of which were spread across some 200 acute hospitals. In these hospitals, some 400 000 operations a year were being performed, accounting for 15% of all elective surgery in the UK. One quarter of all hip replacement operations and one fifth of all heart operations are done in the private sector. The 80 000 other private sector beds are spread across 3000 nursing homes concentrating on elderly handicapped and psychiatric patients. About 10% of the elderly who have surgery are treated in the private sector and this itself constitutes 16% of surgical inpatients in private hospitals. Health insurance has recently been growing at a moderate rate of 4% a year, though it would be surprising if there was not an increase to coincide with the present malaise within the NHS.

In the attempt to reduce waiting lists in the NHS, health authorities are being encouraged to use the spare capacity which exists in the private sector. A recent specific initiative resulted in 4500 patients being transferred from NHS waiting lists for private treatment, paid for by the district health authorities. It is in this area of elective surgery where the NHS is failing, and where the private sector will go on filling the gap unless the NHS puts its own house in order.

Giving patients a statutory right to use other facilities when there is a long wait in their own district is discussed in Chapter 7, on waiting lists. This right rests on using an internal market technique, but it is a mechanism that can stand on its own and could be implemented immediately. Promoting within the NHS an internal market with competing district health authorities is a concept which has considerable potential for improving patients' access to treatment and reducing waiting lists within the NHS. I first became an enthusiast for this approach when visiting Stanford University in California. I was there to give a lecture on a comprehensive nuclear test ban, but I decided to look up Professor Alan Enthoven of the Stanford School of Business who had been writing in a most interesting and iconoclastic manner about the US health system.[2]

I knew that Joseph Califano, who had been President Carter's Secretary for Health Education and Welfare, thought highly of Enthoven's work. But I doubt if I would have felt his views had much relevance for us in Britain if I had not known of him in a previous incarnation in the late 1960s, when he was working in the US Defense Department as one of Robert MacNamara's 'whizz kids' and challenging the conventional wisdom within NATO that was wildly exaggerating the size of the Soviet conventional forces. I quoted Enthoven's view in a book I wrote in 1972, *The Politics of Defence*. So I knew he had unconventional but well-researched opinions.

As we talked and visited a health maintenance unit together, I became deeply impressed with the relevance of what I was seeing and hearing for the NHS. Enthoven told me he had been invited by the Nuffield Trust to visit Britain and we talked about the problems of American academics producing unworkable ideas for impracticable wholesale reform of the NHS. We talked again while he was in Britain. As a former Rhodes Scholar, Enthoven knows Britain well and he did not fall into the trap of proposing reforms for the NHS which had no roots within the existing system. He published his initial views on the internal market in an article amusingly subtitled 'A Man from Mars'. He did not attempt to challenge the ethical basis on which the NHS was founded and he wrote that what he was advocating was a form of 'market socialism'. A DHA would operate within an internal market resembling, he argued, a nationalized company.

It was a totally new way of looking at market forces in health care, for it did not mean reproducing the American health care system in Britain, but taking some of the market disciplines that had, in the US, both reduced health costs and disciplined doctors. His proposals for putting this into practice within the NHS structure[3] were a radical yet evolutionary reform.

The internal market philosophy stems from changes already made in parts of America. US health costs had risen dramatically in the 1970s so that nearly one dollar out of ten spent in the US was going on health care. Alarmed at such cost increases, some started to develop a health plan that would lower costs while actually improving the quality of care. While health costs had of course risen because of an ageing population, most people felt that the cause was the new advances in the science and technology of medicine and the soaring cost of malpractice insurance. These were, however, not the main reasons. Enthoven and others saw that the real reason was that doctors were providing costly services, tests, treatment and operations whether or not patients really needed them and no one was systematically questioning the cost of health since either insurers or government were footing the bills. The way out of this dilemma, Enthoven argued, was not more regulation but more competition, not more government but more intelligent use of government. By forcing doctors to compete for patients, introducing rational economic incentives, demanding more efficient and effective care, we could ultimately reduce health costs to levels that we as a society and as individuals could afford, whether we paid for health care by insurances or through taxes. It was a revelation to hear all this so cogently argued and to realize that it had considerable potential for us in the UK.

It has so far been surprisingly hard to convince the Conservative government of the virtues of the internal market. I have been writing and lecturing about its potential for four years. The SDP has been advocating its experimental introduction since 1984 against a wall of official scepticism. The government's own management board considered the case for the internal market on the basis of the Enthoven model, in which district health authorities would buy and sell services between each other and the private sector in 1986 and concluded that it was impractical. A commitment to introduce an internal market into the NHS was considered for the Conservative election manifesto in 1987, but it was thought then either too risky or too radical or perhaps both. It was, after some hesitation, included in the SDP/Liberal Alliance 1987 manifesto. Its launch during the election campaign was unfortunately rather overshadowed by our health spokesman producing an impressive computer printout illustrative of the number on the hospital waiting lists, then only having to admit under questioning that the names on the printout were actually SDP members. This was too good a story for the press and the finer points of the internal market were lost.

The internal market could be an important counter to the present drive in many DHAs towards self-sufficiency regardless of the cost. The point of the scheme is that the DHA which is not providing the service has to feel the financial consequences of this through paying out money to the DHA or private hospital that does provide the service. This will then act either as an incentive to improve the DHA's efficiency and make extra provision so as to serve patient needs, or make the DHA consciously decide that this particular service to patients will not be provided cost-effectively within the DHA. The internal market also provides a mechanism for allocating resources cost-effectively as well as being a check on the blind pursuit of self-contained self-sufficiency by each and every DHA. Initially, DHAs will need a mechanism for claiming exceptionally from the DHSS centrally in order to meet inescapable and unsupportable transfer costs – but they will eventually be compensated for within the RAWP cross-boundary flow formulae. There should never be an automatic mechanism for financially topping up DHAs from the centre as that would mean losing all the economic pressure for greater efficiency.

The objections to the internal market that the Health Service Management Board focused on in 1986 were threefold. The internal market would, they felt, involve instant implementation of allocations in line with RAWP targets at district level. The answer to this objection is to improve and, where possible, standardize RHA practices in allocating to districts and insist that RHAs loosen the present financial strings by which they still interfere far too frequently with a DHA's financial autonomy.

Another objection was that it would mean abrogating the right of GPs to refer patients to consultants in other districts. The answer to this is first that such clinical freedom can be and is exaggerated. Secondly, it is largely a personal preference system whereby a few GPs traditionally use either the hospital or the consultants whom they know even though they may be outside their DHA boundary. Mostly these GPs themselves practise on the boundary of the DHA. But if GPs were to become part of health teams operating on health maintenance principles within their DHA, instead of autonomous FPCs as at present, they would have a financial incentive in most cases to use their own DHA's facilities for their patients. It would not be necessary in such circumstances formally to abrogate the GPs' right of referral. This right would continue to provide a safety valve. Also, by giving patients statutory rights for referral outside the DHA if the waiting time rises above an average performance figure, flexibility and choice would be maintained. The internal market will not cover all categories of patients and it does not need to be universally applied. It will work where there is enthusiasm for it; in other places where there is little commitment its impact will be slight. But that does not matter – as a technique one of its strengths is that it can have a variable application.

The third argument submitted against the internal market by the Health Service Management Board is that it would require major investment in recording costing and billing systems. The answer to this is that such investment is, in any case, inevitable and necessary if health costs are to be contained. Medical audit within the medical profession increasingly requires such costing information and the NHS is gearing itself up slowly to provide such information. Introducing competitive pressures will simply speed up that process. No one pretends that an internal market can be implemented rapidly, nor is it designed to cover emergency cases. An internal market will be difficult to operate initially and it is helpful that an RHA like East Anglia should set up pilot studies as it has suggested. But the experimental period itself should not be an excuse for delaying implementation of an internal market where managers want it and are ready to develop the financial disciplines which are inherent within it. An internal market will give added impetus to the allocation of resources direct to DHAs. While there are difficulties in calculating cross-boundary flows of patients in inner city DHAs, these should not be exaggerated.

There will need to be special arrangements to recompense patients for travelling costs outside their DHA but that need exists at present, albeit on a smaller scale, and there needs to be generous provision. Admittedly, there are dangers that some DHAs may abandon the aim of self-sufficiency in areas where self-sufficiency is desirable. But all of these problems are soluble and the internal market represents easily the most hopeful new development in NHS thinking. Resource management is providing information which paves the way for the internal market.

The internal market should now be positively endorsed by this Conservative government and it should tell the NHS Management Board to drop its niggardly approach. It is only surprising that Mrs Thatcher should have delayed as long as she has. Perhaps she has prevaricated because she is still tempted to introduce the private insurance system of health care from the US. Yet the mistake many make in comparing the NHS in Britain with the United States health care system is to fail to understand how much the US system is evolving. It is slowly dawning on those who have been long-standing advocates of bringing the American health insurance system to Britain that it would be folly to do this at the very moment when the US is moving away from health insurance and towards managed health care along the lines of health maintenance organizations (HMOs) and preferred provider organizations (PPOs). These are organizations which already account for around 30% of US health care. They occur in many different forms. While they are an interesting development within the US system, even there they are being oversold. They are most appropriate for a healthy population of young earners. They cannot be simply lifted up and transported into the UK system even if that were desirable.

All health systems reflect national characteristics as they evolve within a country; they are not easily transferred, as comes through clearly in Chapter 5 on comparative health care systems. The HMOs manage health care for individuals either from their own internal resources, whether hospitals or clinics, or from outside resources for a fixed annual subscription, or under an insurance policy which restricts the choice of provider because it saves on the cost of provision. The introduction of HMOs represents a considerable change of both philosophy and practice for those used to the item-by-service system of private health insurance. The move towards managed health care has been opposed by the American Medical Association. The reason is that though theoretically it has been a staunch advocate of a market in health care, that was only as long as the market did not produce real competition amongst doctors and did not start to control health care costs.

Some have argued a little too simplistically about the introduction of HMOs in the UK. Even as a pilot project, a fully fledged US version had great difficulty coexisting within the NHS. Perhaps it would be worth a more extensive trial, but a potentially more important development is to take the philosophy behind HMOs into the NHS and design incentives for GPs to operate a group practice from a health centre within a DHA on the basis of HMO attitudes. The existing advantage of the independent contractor status of the GP is its flexibility. It would be possible to adjust the present system to create financial incentives to reward those who manage health care in a way that cuts a DHA's costs. In most cases, where preventive medicine is practised and this leads to early diagnosis, it saves costs by reducing the number of people being admitted to hospital as an inpatient, or if admitted reduces the time spent in hospital. In the US HMOs achieve a 25% lower incidence of hospitalization for their patients. Reinforcing health maintenance attitudes in Britain could bring about considerable savings in a DHA's hospital costs, already the biggest single item in their budget. The skill will be to develop the technique and a system of identifying such a cost-saving and using part of that saving to reward the particular health team, not just doctors, who have made it possible.

Reduction in hospital costs is not just a responsibility of the GP. It must also involve hospital consultants to ensure diagnostic tests are done for outpatients requiring admission to hospital, and that the care of the patient continues not just in hospital but also when discharged. An American HMO investigated the

British system in 1986 and calculated that a 15% cut in hospitalization costs could be brought about using health maintenance methods. Even if it only produced a 5% saving, this would be of considerable benefit to the NHS. The key is to give the whole health team an incentive to bother to persuade people to give up smoking, to reduce weight, to curb their drinking, to control their blood pressure. At the moment in Britain, there is no incentive to practise prevention other than the payment which exists for GPs to give family planning advice and conduct certain screening procedures. The sceptics, and there are many, about introducing HMOs into Britain say with some justice that the NHS is one large HMO. That is true, but it is too large to identify, reward and give incentives to those who maintain people's health cost-effectively. The skill will be to devise within the NHS mechanisms to lift from the US the best from their experience of HMOs. While GPs practise independently of the hospital and particularly operate under a different financial budget, there cannot be an incentive to build in health maintenance attitudes. Some have talked of creating new managed health care organizations.[4] Others envisage small HMOs built around a GP who would manage all aspects of a patient's care. Both approaches can be tried. Introducing health maintenance methods and attitudes inside a DHA would be the best way to start the process. That would complement a competitive internal market between DHAs. The pattern that may be adopted within a DHA could vary considerably and there is room for much experiment. But the precondition, as is argued in Chapter 4 on the future structure of the NHS, is to bring the DHA and FPC together with one shared, cash-limited budget.

Chapter 7

WAITING LISTS

It's the waiting. Once you're in it's terrific. But getting
in there, you wait for an appointment, you wait for
the letter, but once into hospital, the treatment was
fantastic, very, very good.

Patient, 1987

The public concern about the NHS is expressed by 'waiting':
waiting for an appointment; waiting then in hospitals or in
surgeries for the doctor; waiting to come into hospital; waiting at
home for the promised visit. Those who work in the NHS,
particularly doctors, have grown to accept too easily that waiting
is inevitable. Waiting is not inevitable; if that focus of discontent
could be removed, the NHS would be revitalized. Any worthwhile reform of the NHS will start with the question, 'Why are
we waiting?' and will then introduce a series of reforms directed
to minimize waiting time and change the attitude of health
providers to their consumers, the public.

The existence, and persistence, of long waiting times for
treatment is perhaps part of the British traditional acceptance of
queueing. It is extremely doubtful whether any other health
care system in the world would remain so insensitive to such a
glaring indicator of genuine need. It reflects one of the greatest
weaknesses within the structure of the Health Service, namely
the absence of effective consumer pressure. To reduce existing
waiting lists substantially would remove a persistent source of
grievance from within the NHS and a strong focus of criticism
from outside the NHS. It can be done, but only through recognizing and exercising consumers' rights.

For the first twenty-five years of the NHS, close to half a

million people were on lists waiting for hospital admission. From 1973 onwards, waiting lists increased in four distinct steps, three of which coincided with industrial action within the Health Service. The first widespread strike of hospital ancillary workers took place in 1973 and increased waiting lists which had actually fallen during the previous two years. In 1975 both consultants and junior hospital medical staff took industrial action by working to rule, and waiting lists again grew. Lists steadied at around 600 000 people through 1976 and 1977, but then suddenly jumped by 50 000 in the last quarter of 1978. There was no industrial action and that particular rise has never been satisfactorily explained. In 1982 there was further large-scale strike action amongst ancillary workers and waiting lists rose to three quarters of a million.

There cannot be too much surprise that industrial action increases waiting lists since strikes are taken for the purpose of calling attention to grievances through disrupting normal services and, though most people would prefer patients not to suffer, they do suffer, as do schoolchildren when teachers go on strike.

The vast majority of those who wait, either for their initial consultation, having been referred to hospital by their general practitioner, or for subsequent admission to hospital, are due to have surgical operations. These cover five major specialities: general surgery, orthopaedics, gynaecology, ear, nose and throat surgery (ENT), and ophthalmology. They represent what are termed elective surgical cases: admission is not urgent in the sense that delay does not put their life at risk. Delay can, however, often reduce wage packets through not being able to do a normal day's work, for example a docker not being able to lift heavy crates, or being unable to work at all. There is, therefore, an economic cost to waiting lists which is hard to quantify, quite apart from the social cost in terms of pain, inconvenience or misery. Of the general surgical cases, half wait for hernia and varicose vein operations; of the ENT cases, half wait for tonsils and adenoids operations; in orthopaedics, 10% wait for hip replacements. In ophthalmology, cataracts account for about three quarters of those on the waiting list, though one must interpret these particular figures carefully because many eye surgeons put people on the waiting list wanting the cataract to get worse while they wait, not intending to operate for some time after they have been put on the list.

Various attempts have been made to reduce waiting lists, both generally across the NHS as a whole and specifically in certain parts of the country. There has, however, been no sustainable fall in numbers. The most recent failure has been that of the scheme to cut waiting lists by 100 000, from 685 000 to 585 000, in 1987–8. In the first six months of this scheme, waiting lists went up in nine regions and down in only four, despite a specific cash injection of £25 million and 350 special schemes being authorized. It appears that, while 100 000 more patients were seen, surgeons, in part because of lack of funding, had to reduce the number of cases that they treated. The Central Committee for Hospital Medical Services has estimated that in 1987, over 3000 acute beds were closed in England and Wales as a response to financial circumstances. Overall, it claims 5300 beds were closed and 900 new beds opened, and that while 30% were closed as part of implementing existing strategic plans and a further 11% due to rationalization, the remaining 59% were due to financial constraints.

Given this history, it is not surprising that a resigned acceptance of waiting lists has developed. Indeed, at times waiting lists have been rationalized as an inevitable and necessary manifestation of a supposed infinite demand. What's in a waiting list? ask the cynics – disparaging anomalies and inconsistencies within the lists. This view persists despite the fact that there have been strikingly successful initiatives to reduce waiting lists, then to maintain waiting lists at a much reduced level. This has been done for example in South Tees Health Authority, admittedly with £266 000 from the government's waiting list initiative, but that helped achieve the introduction of a bed manager or waiting list coordinator. This manager was able to maintain an up-to-date list of people available, contacting them by telephone and filling cancellations. In this way, 888 cases were removed from a list of 1150 during eight months with a total of 740 operations – and the total cost was £299 per patient. Once the five-day ward was used for other specialities, the non-urgent waiting list for general surgery rose again, but only to half its previous size.

This experience gives the lie to the comfortable belief that in all cases demand is infinite. Infinite demand is an excuse. There are some areas where demand is genuinely infinite and some GPs do simply expand their referral rates to fill up waiting lists that start to come down, but the extent of this can be, and frequently is, exaggerated. Another excuse is that the statistical basis on which lists are compiled is too frequently inaccurate for the numbers to be taken seriously. Though there are considerable inaccuracies, when systematic attempts are made to remove these, the fall in numbers rarely fulfils expectations.

Few subjects are more susceptible to instant solutions through anecdotal evidence or press exposure. Everyone can agree that something was wrong when Mr Tebbit, while chairman of the Conservative Party, visited a friend in a forty-two-bed eye hospital and drew attention to the fact that there were only four patients in the hospital on a particular Thursday afternoon when there were 1500 patients on the waiting list. Similarly, everyone knew something was wrong when Mr Harris, an orthopaedic surgeon at St Mary's Hospital, Paddington, having appeared at a Conservative Party press conference during the 1987 general election, extolling the merits of Conservative health policy, was photographed by the press a few months later in an empty new ward which was then unable to open because of lack of money. There are on average 50 000 acute beds empty each day in NHS hospitals. That is a resource which could clearly be better utilized. Better management of waiting lists nationwide is needed, not an express service for those who pay.

The challenge in tackling lengthy waiting times is that there is no easily discernible explanation as to why they occur. There is no direct relationship to show that district health authorities with large waiting lists waste their bed allocation. One would expect that, given the immense variation in waiting lists across district health authorities, one could find some common factors. But this is not so. The average surgeon has 200 people on their waiting list, but a few surgeons have ten times that number. Some orthopaedic surgeons operate on 100 cases each year while others operate on 750. There is a threefold variation in the provision of beds, and a tenfold variation in number of support staff, between equivalent district health authorities. We know that the appointment of a new consultant surgeon can be mirrored after two or three years by a growth in the waiting list, whereas another new consultant appointment can lead to a sustained reduction in waiting lists. Districts with a high proportion of elderly people do not have, as one would expect, longer waiting lists for cataract operations. Even in those districts where there is a shortage of beds in relation to population, there are not always larger waiting lists. There is also little evidence to support the theory that waiting lists mirror large inflows of patients from neighbouring districts.

Against such a confusing background of statistics, it is hardly surprising that many people have despaired of finding a rational solution to the waiting list problem. Despair gives plenty of scope for the dogmatists. Those who believe in a private health care market see the introduction of private health insurance as the only way of reducing waiting lists for all except the poor. Those who are hostile to private medicine blame its presence for fuelling waiting lists. They either want to ban private health care completely or stop consultants from practising within the NHS if they also work in the private sector. There is certainly a financial incentive for a surgeon practising privately to maintain a large NHS surgical waiting list. But there is not much hard statistical evidence that the existence of private medicine alongside the NHS is a major factor in maintaining large NHS waiting lists.

Indeed, there is a growing public acceptance that the private sector should be used where private hospitals have spare capacity to reduce NHS waiting lists. Bath Health Authority paid for 100 children on the ENT lists to be treated at a private clinic for operations on tonsils and adenoids. The cost was greater than being treated within the NHS, but they felt able to justify this extra cost. York Health Authority contracted out sterilization operations to the private sector because of a long waiting list. Surgeons at St Bartholomew's Hospital in London cleared more than 175 children from the waiting list for tonsillectomies in 1986 by taking over two floors of the private Princess Grace Hospital and operating throughout the four-day Easter holiday weekend. In 1985–6 over £5 million was spent by health authorities on contracting out arrangements. It is important that health authorities do not over-use the private sector since there is an obvious danger of a DHA becoming dependent on the private sector and then finding the private sector costs rising as they feel able to ask a higher price.

What is extraordinary, given the plethora of working parties established at every level throughout the NHS, is that there has been only one national working party to study waiting lists. This was established in 1979 to cover orthopaedic waiting lists under the chairmanship of Professor Sir Robert Duthie. The membership was chosen initially by the Labour government, and then checked but kept unchanged by the incoming Conservative government. Before the working group started, there were 112 999 orthopaedic patients on the inpatient waiting list, and 32% of the non-urgent cases had waited over one year for admission. Four years later, in 1983, the total orthopaedic waiting list had risen to 142 113 and 40% had waited for over a year.

Just before the 1987 general election, the government announced its £50 million waiting list initiative. It was to consist of two yearly tranches of £25 million, and health authorities have had to make specific bids for money each year. There have been some successes, but overall the March 1987 figure of 680 000 people on the waiting list is not likely to be reduced by the 100 000 predicted. The problem is that just as some health authorities were about to invest this new money to reduce waiting lists, they were having to cut back on their existing budgets with the effect of increasing waiting lists. West Berkshire Health Authority received £95 000 to take 900 patients off the waiting list, but because of a projected over-spend of £1.3 million, they had to postpone operations for 3000 patients waiting for gynaecology, orthopaedic, ENT, eye and general surgery. Doncaster Health Authority received £22 000 to treat 470 patients, but a projected overspend of £700 000 forced the closure of 69 beds and the temporary suspension of two wards which delayed 1000 operations. The South Western Region and Merseyside appear to have been successful in reducing waiting lists, but South East Thames, Oxford, West Midlands and Yorkshire all received money only to see their waiting lists increase. One particularly successful authority has been Sheffield, which hopes to have reduced its waiting list by 1000 after an allocation of £800 000. Overall this experience shows yet again how difficult it is to reduce waiting lists, even with extra money, and if districts are unable to live within their budgets, there is little point in the government giving with one hand and taking with the other.

Few people have given more time and thought to studying the problem of waiting lists than John Yates[1] and he has suggested a number of worthwhile initiatives. Making available the factual information about waiting lists to the public at large through local newspapers is a key pressure which can stimulate local MPs and community health councils to demand that district health authorities take action. It is certainly worth applying these pressures and the College of Health has done much to stimulate consumer awareness by publishing league tables on waiting lists. The government's new readiness to publish statistics comparing hospitals is also a very welcome addition to consumer knowledge, and through knowledge to mobilizing consumer pressure for action.

The suggestion that there should be a health inspectorate covering acute hospitals to review quality and quantity of treatment is sensible but not new. It could operate in much the same way that the Health Advisory Service covers geriatric hospitals and hospitals for the mentally ill, though it could beneficially use some of the techniques used by the National Development Team for the Mentally Handicapped. If it were to concentrate initially on hospitals with high waiting lists and suggest ways of reducing them, it would provide an objective outside pressure, particularly if the results were published. It must have the right to report differences, in particular in consultants' performance, and question clinical practices that have cost and management implications. Publication would also provide a focus for the community health council to champion improved performance. But inspection has hitherto been resisted by medical and surgical consultants in the acute hospitals as being too intrusive into their clinical judgement, and by the district health authorities as eroding their managerial functions. Important though such new initiatives are, they are essentially aimed at improving existing procedures within the present framework. They do not challenge that framework; they do not introduce

115

market disciplines nor raise the voice and power of the consumer to exercise a right to treatment. It is hard to escape the conclusion that, unless the long-suffering patient on the waiting list is given rights and, therefore, the power to seek an alternative, excessively long waiting lists will continue to bedevil the National Health Service.

Throughout the recent passage of the Health and Medicines legislation, the SDP argued that patients should have a statutory right, varied from time to time by Regulation, to obtain treatment after specified periods of waiting. At the moment, a patient can be referred by their family doctor to a consultant operating outside the district health authority in which the patient resides. But such referrals are at the GP's discretion and are not made as a patient's right. Nor are DHAs with small waiting lists always keen to take on patients from outside their own district when they are well aware that they receive no direct reimbursement and are given any financial compensation only as a result of a cross-boundary reallocation within the RAWP formula.

What is needed is a rational, quantifiable basis for the right of a patient to be referred elsewhere and the right of the DHA treating them to be financially recompensed. That right could be triggered when the waiting time for a particular category of treatment, either for a consultant appointment or an actual treatment, exceeds the average in the best 20% of district health authorities. In this way, a health authority would have a yardstick to live up to and the patient would have a limit placed on the length of time that they would have to wait. If waiting lists were reduced further in the best 20%, that is, the top thirty-eight district health authorities, so the yardstick would move down in the district health authorities where waiting lists were high. The mechanism would be self-adjusting within the NHS. Such a system is wholly compatible with, and would operate well within, a fully fledged internal market between district health authorities for most forms of treatment. But it can, and should, be brought into operation well in advance of the full development of an internal market. It does not need all the complicated financial assessments for comparative costings. It can operate within the existing framework. It would become even more necessary as a safeguard for patients if the general practitioner were operating within a combined FPC DHA budget, for the general practitioner would have an interest in using that DHA.

The financial incentive for a district health authority to reduce its waiting lists below the trigger point would be that it would have to pay the district health authority in which the statutory right to treatment was exercised, and to do so within months, out of its annual budget. Given the present under-funding of the NHS, this imposition of extra costs in some DHAs could be crippling. It would therefore be necessary for the government to make the existing waiting-list fund subject to claims by DHAs, but only in cases where the DHA could demonstrate that its inability to stay within the best 20% yardstick was beyond its control. The existence of such a financial penalty would be an incentive on all concerned in the district health authority – doctors as well as administrators – to reduce their waiting lists.

A further discipline that would operate on all district health authorities' costs would be that, provided the cost of the treatment was no higher than in an available district health authority, a family doctor could refer a patient exercising their statutory right for treatment to the private sector, particularly if that would mean less travelling because the patient would be treated in a private hospital within their own health district. This would encourage the private sector and district health authorities to keep their costs down. Some DHAs would develop more extensive facilities for certain treatments other than those necessary for their own population, even to developing centres specializing in specific treatments like hip replacement operations. This would bring advantages since there is no doubt that with a high throughput considerable expertise is built up.

The problem is that, if uncontrolled, this mechanism could lead to DHAs offering too limited a service and patients being expected to travel much too far. The problems of travel costs are already becoming severe for the families of young babies transferred out of the district for specialized intensive care. The present arrangements are deeply unsatisfactory. Even if the family are claiming income support, it is very difficult to receive any help as there is no automatic right. The correct place to put the burden of paying for travel costs is with the patient's own

DHA. Health authorities may not have or want sufficient facilities to treat their own patients. The criteria for eligibility to claim travel costs should be national and similar to the criteria for exemption from prescription charges.

We already know that where existing waiting lists have been successfully reduced, it has often been accompanied by changes in practice – such as surgical operations hitherto conducted as an inpatient being conducted as an outpatient – or where a special intensive effort has been made to carry out a large number of surgical procedures using some of the economies of scale and the efficiencies of a high throughput. It is noticeable that these techniques are more often found in the private sector than within the National Health Service. Yet there is no reason why these same cost-effective techniques should not be applied. They are methods that are used by doctors when practising privately but sometimes not when practising in the NHS.

What is needed is a mechanism for forcing these changes of practice on to the NHS. The only mechanism that will work is to give the patients the right to go elsewhere for treatment at no cost to themselves and give a financial incentive to the patient's own DHA to provide an adequate service.

Chapter 8

COMMUNITY CARE

Appropriate care should be provided for individuals in such a way as to enable them to lead as normal an existence as possible given their particular disabilities and to minimize disruption of life within their community.

House of Commons Social Services
Committee Report, *Community Care*, 1984/5

Community care touches on far more than the NHS and the personal social services as run by local government. It involves housing, transport, education and even, on occasions, employment policy. It concerns predominantly, though by no means exclusively, the elderly, the mentally ill, and the mentally handicapped. Its main purpose is to enable the transition to take place – from institutional care to care at home – and, even more importantly, to sustain and enrich care in the home. It should enable individuals to have the greatest possible degree of choice in how they live their own lives. The opportunities and the successes of an enlightened community care policy can be seen around us in every walk of life. Sadly, so too can the neglect and failures of an impoverished community care programme; a programme impoverished not just in terms of financial support, but in terms of treating people as individuals and respecting their wishes and their judgement.

Too often the vulnerable, particularly the elderly and the disabled, are made to feel that they are lucky to be given any help, that it is not an entitlement but something made available out of the goodness of heart of either central or local government. Those who are frail and infirm need particular sensitivity and encouragement if they are to ask for what they want or to express their personal preferences. It is all too easy for the professionals to trample unwittingly on these people's privacy, self-respect and autonomy; particularly easy when the caring professions themselves are struggling with workloads which do not allow them to give that most precious ingredient of all, their time, to listen and take note of an individual's special circumstances. Many of these people are hard of hearing, which makes it just that little bit more difficult to communicate sensitively and to encourage full participation. Often their memory is not what it was and sometimes their IQ is low. All of these features make community care a highly desirable aspiration but one which is immensely difficult to fulfil.

It was in recognition of the financial pressures placed on local authority services as a result of pushing the concept of care in the community that, in 1976, the Labour government introduced a new finance mechanism known as joint funding. This was a means of allowing a limited use of NHS resources for the purpose of funding local government services, where this was likely to yield a better return to the community than if the service had been developed solely by the NHS. Essentially, it was an arrangement for using NHS funds to support local government spending. At the time of its introduction, it also provided the financial support to make a reality of joint planning between the coterminous local government social services departments and the area health authority planning structure which had started to operate in 1974. It had the potential for easing long-standing pressure points and problems where their responsibilities overlapped, particularly in the Cinderella areas of mental illness, mental handicap and care of the elderly. I was well aware at the time that if the best local government councillors were to serve on the joint planning machinery with the NHS, it must dispose hard cash. Otherwise they would let other less influential councillors serve on the committees, confident in the belief that they would become mere talking shops.

The joint funding proposals as announced in 1976 allowed for both capital and revenue support to be given to joint schemes, and assumed that at the end of the period of joint funding, which was usually five years, one of the partners would, by previous agreement, take on responsibility for funding the service. Over the past decade, joint funding has been of major importance in enabling us to finance the move away from institutional care, and the subsequent development of community care. It has supported the development of many innovative projects, and helped create genuine local government/health authority cooperation to a much greater extent than ever before.

The number of mental illness beds in hospital has been reduced by 25 000 over the last decade, and fewer than 64 000 people are now resident in psychiatric hospitals, though there were some 200 000 admissions to and discharges from psychiatric hospitals. It is thought that sixty psychiatric hospitals are likely to close in the next ten years and probably over 20 000 people with a history of hospital care for their mental illness will need to be supported and cared for in the community. It is clear that community mental health services are not expanding anywhere near fast enough to match the past and projected hospital closure programme. We need a special bridging fund, which MIND has suggested should be £50 million in the first year rising to £500 million, as an addition to normal finance. It could be buttressed by the sale of these hospital sites. Without a community development fund, it will be impossible to make the transition from hospital to community care.

Considerable though its initial achievements were, the House of Commons Social Services Select Committee was probably right to conclude that in its original form 'as a means of transferring further responsibilities from the NHS to local authorities, joint funding was virtually played out',[1] although less than 1% of the 1984/5 joint funding programme was made up of 1983/4 projects resubmitted. However, the trend towards greater health authority funding of projects after the five-year period, and therefore of reduced local government funding, reflects not only a willingness on the part of the Health Service to take greater responsibility for community services, but also the acute financial constraints in which many local authorities find themselves.

Joint finance currently accounts for only 1% of health authority budgets and only 8.8% of joint financing goes on mental health projects. Dowry payments made for each year for a patient discharged from hospital to a local authority or voluntary organization are running near to £12 million a year. Dowry payments are not geared to cover the cost of an individual's disability and need to be extended and made more flexible. This is thrown into sharp relief by the report of Sir Roy Griffiths into community care.[2] For implicit in it is the need for considerably more resources than are at present allocated. Yet all governments' previous record in this field does not give much room for optimism.

The other major criticism aimed at joint funding is that those developments which are submitted and funded do not always adequately reflect the needs of the people using the services. Rather they are the result of a power game between different professionals which acts as a block to consumer involvement within the planning process. While such criticisms may be overstating the problem, it nevertheless is a cause of some concern that consumers have not played a larger part in the development of projects for submission for joint funding.

The Griffiths Report leaves unanswered many questions about the future of joint funding. It proposes the financing of community services through a community care grant, and through top-sliced grants for particular innovations. However, by suggesting the establishment of lead agencies to coordinate the development of services in the community, it appears to question the future of joint funding. Yet even if Griffiths' recommendations were to be implemented in full, which appears unlikely, there would still be a need for joint working between local authorities and health authorities, and for funding to facilitate this. Such funding, together with other sources of finance, will be essential if we are to ensure that community care does not remain, in Griffiths' terms, 'a poor relation'.

The increasing number of elderly people poses the major challenge to community care policy. By 1991, in England and Wales, there will be 15% more people aged 75 and older than there were in 1981, and 30% more people aged 85 and over. One of the major problems associated with ageing is senile dementia, which afflicts 10% of those aged over 65 and 22% of those over 80. Local authorities are spending well over £1 billion a year on residential care and community services directly for the elderly – mainly on home helps, day care, meals-on-wheels, sheltered housing. These services account for some 45% of total social services expenditure. By far the majority of elderly people fend for themselves or are looked after adequately by relatives, friends or the voluntary sector without turning to the local authority social services for support. Residential care is provided for around 2% of those over 65 years old and support in the community for a further 13%.

It has been estimated that 90% of the mentally ill and 80% of the mentally handicapped are cared for full-time by their families. This is an amazing figure for it cannot be ignored how stressful such care can be, particularly in coping with schizophrenics. Indeed, so difficult is care in some cases that people have come to recognize that there is a larger role for sheltered residential care than has been hitherto recognized. Were family carers steadily to shift the responsibility on to local and central government, it would be impossible to cope. Yet, if families are willing to accept such responsibilities, they need far more help. The traditional nuclear family of a married couple with children and relatives living nearby in the same community is changing fast. Only 15% of households comprise a married man with a dependent wife and two children. One third of all marriages end in divorce. Many people who divorce then remarry and have an extended and complicated pattern of relationships. Over 60% of married women are employed outside the home. Mobility in search of employment or improved living standards has meant that children are increasingly not remaining in their home towns after marriage and are leaving ageing parents behind in this process. If such a new pattern of family life – a pattern which is largely irreversible – is to be encouraged to accept the responsibility to care for relatives, it will need more complex support arrangements than exist at present. There is more chance, for instance, that daughters will take up their responsibility to look after relatives if they can continue to work meanwhile. That means more daytime support being provided during the working week than was ever needed when more women stayed at home and did not have jobs.

If self-fulfilment is to be the theme of social support, then the individuals being supported must be treated as individuals with their own self-respect. At the heart of any successful policy for community care is the weight given to the individual's choice as to what they want to do, rather than the collective decision as to what others think is best for them. It is a difficult question whether the views and wishes of the person for whom care is designed should predominate, or whether the professional judgement and preferences of the designer of a particular pattern of care should take precedence. That dilemma is clearly and, although I disagree with his judgement, refreshingly identified in the second report of Sir Roy Griffiths to the Secretary of State for Social Services, *Community Care – Agenda for Action*:

> The Audit Commission highlighted the policy conflicts and perverse incentives which exist in the impact of supplementary benefit payments for residential care on community care policies. This particular benefit is at the interface between the social security open-ended financial commitment based on entitlement and a budgeted provision against priority of need, which is the social services approach. Prima facie the two approaches are diametrically opposed.

They are indeed opposed, and what is at issue is a principle which goes to the root of many of the other choices which confront us over community care. Who does know best? The individual being cared for or the professional adviser or carer? Towards whom in the last analysis should a policy be tilted? The Griffiths approach that can be read on the face of his report, but more often between the lines, deserves to be decisively rejected. By suggesting that the social worker should decide, Griffiths tilts the balance in favour of the professional carer determining what is in the best interests of the individual. In particular that will be the sole determining factor if the individual happens to be poor. In a community care system that values freedom and choice, the balance should be tilted in favour of the individual deciding, regardless of whether they are poor or rich.

In all the various discussions that are now in progress over the direction of community care, this fundamental philosophical question has to be determined first. If government decides, as it should, in favour of the individual, professionals will remain as now – only advisers, albeit crucial ones. If government regrettably chooses in favour of the professional deciding, then it becomes a secondary question where the responsibility for making this ultimate decision should lie. Should it be concentrated on the local authority as Griffiths recommends, a conclusion which is probably inescapable if one accepts his premise; or alternatively, should responsibility be spread across a number of decision-makers cooperating in the field of community care? If the individual is still to decide, cooperation might be less coherent, but leaving people to shop around, to make the decision they want, has certain advantages.

The prior question as to who is to decide, individual or professional, is pre-eminently a political one and it has extremely interesting ideological roots. It poses for the present Conservative government a major dilemma, for all its rhetoric is to emphasize individual freedom. Its ideological leaning, we are told, is towards choice. Yet, time and time again, its actions belie both its rhetoric and ideology; it plumps in the interests of economy for centralized direction. Sir Roy Griffiths wants to restrict through cash limits the present largely open-ended entitlement of elderly or handicapped people to residential accommodation. He does not want to continue, in effect, an open entitlement – subject to a means test – to residential care through social security financial support.

The Wagner Committee,[3] while agreeing with many of Griffiths' detailed proposals, nevertheless emphasizes consumer choice. It wants the social security system to provide support, whether in a person's home or in a residential home, in such a way that they have an open, positive choice, irrespective of their income. The Wagner Committee was 'much attracted to the idea of issuing community care allowances to people with special needs, to be used by them to procure care services of their choice'.

Griffiths appears to believe that there is a large pool of money for community care available if social security financial support for people in residential homes was constrained. He produces no actual evidence for this belief. Yet independent research from the Social Policy Research Unit at York University has

125

shown that 93% of those in residential accommodation were appropriately placed at the time of admission. Only one person from a group of 200 people admitted from hospital was judged not to be in need of residential accommodation. There was evidence that some people could have returned to or remained in the community if appropriate services, particularly sheltered housing, had been available. But a DHSS working party[4] concluded on the basis of these findings, 'Nevertheless, the results provide little support for the view that a large proportion of elderly people are inappropriately placed in private or voluntary residential homes.'

The working party thought that there were reasons for having assessments even if only a small number of entrants were 'diverted to more appropriate forms of care'. But the price for a little diversion is, in effect, coercion. Certainly it is worth trying to ensure that only those who need residential accommodation are using it, and those who can where possible are persuaded and encouraged to remain at home. But no allocation system is perfect and in this case, since self-allocation is not working badly, why destroy it?

A far more important anomaly affecting residential accommodation, with greater financial implications, stems from the fact that it is often a matter of chance whether a person needing long-stay care finds themself in a nursing home, a residential home, or a geriatric ward. All have different costs and charging arrangements. It is hard to understand why the NHS should pick up the bill for all patients regardless of their means; local authorities charge their well-off residential patients and the DHSS restricts income support for those in private and voluntary homes to patients with assets of less than £6000. This matter is dealt with in more detail in Chapter 10, Paying for the NHS.

Even the Griffiths Report states, 'The present provision of social security for residential care is not wholly bad; the unintentional consequence of government action has been to provide accommodation for large numbers of people, many of whom would have needed it, and by international comparisons we do not as yet have excessive numbers of people in residential accommodation.' An alternative way of expressing the same situation would be to say that during the last decade more and

126

more elderly or handicapped people, finding it hard to manage at home, irrespective of income, have had the option to live in a local authority, or independent-voluntary, or privately run, home. The number using these independent homes has more than doubled and almost 50% of all residents are financed by social security payments available as of right to individuals who cannot afford to pay the cost of treatment themselves. This represents an extension of freedom of choice in a most interesting way. Through the social security system, we have developed what is in effect a workable voucher system.

Why would anyone want to break up such a system? Yet that is what we are perilously close to doing. Mrs Thatcher has shown a marked distaste for the Griffiths proposals and it is widely thought that this is due to his recommendation that local government social services departments should be given so powerful a role in community care that they would, in effect, become the deciders. It would be compatible with both Mrs Thatcher's rhetoric and her ideology if in fact she has blanched not just because of the local authority involvement, but over the effect of Griffiths' recommendation in restricting freedom of choice. Let us hope that that is the case.

What needs to be done with the Griffiths recommendations is to reassert the primacy of consumer choice. We should acknowledge that people have been shunted from hospital institutional care out into the 'community', often ending up in residential homes, without any serious consideration given to caring for them in a home of their own. Also that because of the inadequacies of support facilities for living at home, too many people have been encouraged or forced to go into residential accommodation. But instead of scrapping the system of entitlement, as Griffiths suggests, social security should continue to operate as a means-tested allowance for residential and nursing home care, currently running at £130–£185 a week respectively, and extend new allowances to cover other forms of community care, a 'carer's allowance'.

Entitlements worked out in this way would be in marked contrast to the Griffiths proposals under which individuals without their own resources would be constrained to accept whatever they were offered. Griffiths pays lip service to consumer choice but nowhere in the report is there any mention of a right to question professional decisions or a right to receive services outside the geographical boundaries of the funding local authority. For the poor, there would in effect be no choice. It having been decided for them that they needed or did not need a particular form of care, they would have little option but to acquiesce. That would give the social services very considerable control over a large number of people's lives. To return to that degree of bureaucratic control is not exactly an extension of freedom. Nor do the proponents of such a step give any figures for the money that they expect to save. It is not likely to be much. Assessment of need is part of providing good professional advice and is to be encouraged. In most cases, an individual advised to remain in the community, and with a package devised to help them do so, will freely decide to remain. But assessment should not be pointed like a gun to the head of vulnerable people.

By allowing the social security system to continue to pay residential costs on a means-tested basis and grant a new means-tested entitlement to carer's benefit, the state would be extending freedom and creating genuine choice. If the state wants to curb abuse, then the suggested independent inspectorate should be empowered to question the placement of individuals in residential accommodation and ask for a reassessment of whether or not they should be returned to the community. Putting the onus of proof that way round is certainly a more attractive proposition than placing the burden of an appeal on the individuals who may be frightened or feel incapable of putting their case.

A social security system able to challenge the need for someone to be in residential accommodation must also be able to offer a financial entitlement to help someone remain in their own home. Such a carer's allowance would encourage people, at a lower cost to the social security system, to remain at home rather than to choose residential accommodation. It cannot be assumed in all cases that the total cost to the NHS, to social security and to the local authority, of remaining at home will be less than choosing residential accommodation. The Audit Commission showed that at one extreme, community care expenditure is nearly four times as high as expenditure on residential care, and at the other, residential services account for a level of expenditure about twice as high as community care. The social security system has, however, a vested interest in creating a means-tested carer's allowance, while they are offering a virtually open-ended residential board-and-lodging allowance that will help the vast majority who would prefer to stay at home to do so.

Social security should ensure the carer's allowance is available for anyone whom the social services single agency had assessed as being in need of financial assistance in order to be cared for at home. This allowance would be in addition to any income support and housing benefit to which they were entitled. At present there is little other than constant-attendance allowance to help someone financially to opt to remain at home if they need continuous care, and pay someone to help them at home.

The government is already in a serious mess as a result of the impact of the April 1988 social security changes on the severely disabled. This is because the disability and severe disability pensions will be more difficult to claim than the previous weekly additions to supplementary benefit for special heating, diet, laundry and other special requirements. It hurriedly had to spatchcock together in 1988 an Independent Living Fund, endowed with up to £5 million for the first year, to ease the transition problems. Though welcome, it only underlines the need for a more permanent and comprehensive carer's allowance. Though the criteria have still to be sorted out, the fund will be able to make regular payments to disabled people to meet their special costs and be an addition to their other benefit entitlements. The Disablement Income Group have somewhat reluctantly agreed to cooperate with the running of the fund, fearing that a refusal to do so would exacerbate the inadequacy of the arrangements for meeting the costs of disability.

Under a carer's allowance, it would be for social security to determine against specific criteria what should be paid out. But in most cases, the allowance would be preventing someone from going into residential care and therefore the sums of money involved would be a lot less than the cost to social security of having to provide for residential board-and-lodging charges, particularly if nursing care is involved. It would not therefore be in their interests to discourage social services departments from advising their clients to apply for a carer's allowance. This underlines again the advantage of keeping functions of social services and social security separate. The task of social services is to encourage the individual either to stay at home or to go into residential accommodation, based on their professional judgement. The choice is the individual's. The decision over what to pay in a carer's allowance, as with residential board-and-lodging costs, is for social security, not social services. Such an enabling role for the social services department is wholly compatible with their professional skills as assessors and advisers, but they are not and should not become the deciders, particularly on matters relating to benefit entitlements. As is the case at present, the policing of social security would remain a matter for them and should not involve social services. Just as they can and do refuse payments at present, so they could refuse while subject to appeal to pay carer's benefit or a claim under income support to pay residential costs. Neither of these entitlements would be cash limited, but like most of the social security system, an indirect cash limit operates in the extent to which they decide to challenge entitlements.

In such a system the social security entitlement would be financially neutral, neither encouraging someone to choose residential accommodation nor discouraging them from staying at home, and there is a much better chance that objective need would prove to be the main deciding point. In this structure, the social services professional advice and assessment would be crucial. But the social workers would not be deciders. That decision would be taken by the individual and their closest relatives. Social services departments have never wanted to be embroiled in decisions over income support. They have hitherto argued that though they can advise, they should not be the deciders, and that should be undertaken by social security officers in the local branch of the DHSS. The Social Fund is going to put enough strain on social workers trying to help people to repay loans or find other resources without adding this additional and inappropriate role.

Money is the carrot that Griffiths is offering the social services authorities for taking on the responsibility for assessing whether a move to residential accommodation 'was in the best interests of the individual and what the local authority would be prepared to pay for'. Fortunately, some in local government with long experience of Labour as well as Conservative governments are showing a healthy scepticism that they will ever be granted anything other than a paltry portion of the social security budget that might be saved by taking on this responsibility. They also see it as a heavy price to pay for identifying social services departments with the old 'Poor Law' mentality which many of them thankfully gave up decades ago.

This particular Griffiths recommendation is a mistaken policy because it is a poor system for poor people. It fails to recognize that we do have an obligation under our social security system to fund residential care for that generation of pensioners who will never have the level of pension through the state scheme that will enable them to meet residential costs unless they have in addition their own personal financial resources. It is also mistaken because it is abandoning a voucher system of choice, just at the moment when more and more pensioners will be able to meet the cost of residential accommodation from their own resources and will not be entitled to, or need help from, income support. At present, nearly half of all heads of households over sixty-five are homeowners. Yet of that generation presently between thirty and fifty-nine, nearly two thirds own their own homes. Future pensioners will in addition have occupational pensions and more will have insurance policies to cover the costs of chronic illness. More of the new generation of elderly will be able to pay the economic cost of community services and will be readier to do so. In return, they have the right to expect better, active rehabilitation facilities if they are struck down by a stroke and temporarily paralysed. They will want more importance given to services to keep them mobile and will expect to be treated as full citizens, actively contributing to society. They want independence, not dependence, and they should be encouraged to make economic choices to achieve that end.

All these trends argue for staying with the present system of means-tested entitlement and individual choice and not reverting to a system based on needs assessment and collective direction. We are meant to be moving away from a 'nanny knows best' society and one hopes that Mrs Thatcher's lukewarm reception to this Second Griffiths Report, which is in itself a marked contrast to her enthusiastic endorsement of the first report over general managers, is an indication that the government is prepared to think again.

An enlightened community care policy should orientate itself to enabling the individual to live a full life. To do that effectively, means embracing the philosophy consistently advocated by the SDP of a carer's charter allied to a carer's allowance so as to create a model of community care where the individual is sovereign and the professionals are more enablers than deciders. If this model is adopted, then there is far less of a case for a formal transfer of responsibilities from existing decision-makers to local government social services departments. A carer's charter means the sharing of responsibilities, but it does also mean a single coordinator, preferably behind a single door. It is here that the Griffiths recommendation for a 'single access agency', whereby social services departments are charged with the responsibility for drawing up, and hopefully for implementing, an individual care plan, makes sense. But not all the skills, particularly the management skills, lie in the social services departments. Yet transferring people from the DHAs will prove to be very difficult and likely to provoke some opposition from people and services that were previously under local government.

In practice, it may well be sensible to have mixed manning of a single agency. Cooperation is anyhow going to be inevitable, for no scheme will end all the overlapping functions. It is not as if we can spare skilled social workers with care experience for managerial roles, particularly those who have the wide-based experience and generic training rather than only specialized skills that will be needed in a single access agency. Social workers with knowledge of children's legislation are increasingly involved in child abuse and a variety of statutory requirements. Will the training of social workers be expanded? Will the managerial training be provided? All one can do is to flag a deep concern about paper plans. Individual care plans will take precious time needing, wherever possible, to involve the person to be cared for, relatives, guardians, executors or just close friends, voluntary organizations, private sector carers and public authorities like the NHS, social security, housing and in the case of children and young adults, education, and the Manpower Services Commission.

People in search of a care package must know where to go and must have confidence that the agency responsible will have the authority to bring together the constituent parts of the package. Here, the Griffiths recommendation for a minister of state in the DHSS to be clearly identified as being responsible for community care is well thought out and essential. Such a minister would have to be supported by a designated group of senior officials, including those with responsibility for community care finance, community care policy, the operational distribution and monitoring of central government funds for community care and the national inspection of standards of service provision. That would give the necessary powers to ensure that the social service departments have the necessary clout across all the administrative and financial divisions within community care, not only to design an individual package, but to make its constituent parts hold together. Without this, the design could be faultless but its execution flawed.

The whole package, for example, for keeping in the community someone with multiple sclerosis whose bladder has been affected could fall apart if access to a frequent laundry service to help with incontinence did not materialize; or if a daytime and evening sitting service failed to keep to its time commitments so that the daughter who was looking after her mother or father could no longer hold down her job; or if the failure to honour a pledge to provide a residential place by the DHA to allow the full-time carer to take a holiday precipitated them to give up and seek a less demanding job. It will be the capacity to mobilize all appropriate and available resources, from chiropody services, meals-on-wheels, transport, ramps and rails for the disabled, telephones, wardens, home helps, incontinence pads, community nurses, health visitors and social workers, that will be the determining factors between success or failure.

In 1976, meals-on-wheels were provided at a rate of 17 000 per thousand over-75s; a decade later, the rate had dropped to 14 600 per thousand over-75s. Yet the provision of such hot meals once a day can make all the difference for an old person unable to cook as to whether they stay at home or go into residential accommodation. Over that same period, day care per thousand over-75s rose until 1982 but then started to fall back. Home helps throughout that decade have not increased overall, despite considerable shortages all over the country. Housing authorities are still not linking up old people's homes with inter-coms or arranging for part-time wardens. Some are often reluc-tant to move families closer together in order to make it easier for the younger part of the family to help care for their elderly relatives. Transport services are also often so inadequate that visiting becomes harder and attendance at day centres difficult.

Many hospitals and nursing homes are still reluctant to accept that they have a responsibility to help provide a break for carers, taking people in to allow 'respite' leave for carers. Evening and daytime sitting services have not been introduced in many areas, with local authorities attached to the more formalized warden arrangements which are expensive and not always easy to establish. The rhetoric of community care has, as is so often the case, not been matched with resources. The problem with com-munity care is that everyone agrees it is a good thing, but that very consensus acts as a veil to cover over continued under-provision.

Chapter 9

PUBLIC HEALTH

If you have disfiguring lesions on your face, you're ulcerated from your mouth to your anus and you're producing ten litres of diarrhoea a day – to encourage you to be brave and carry on living with dignity is going to take considerable skill in my opinion.

Nurse in an AIDS hospice, 1988[1]

A few years ago, the conventional wisdom was that the days of epidemics involving serious illnesses were over. Now, with the lurking threat surrounding AIDS, we face an epidemic whose full extent none of us can assuredly predict. 'What the number will eventually be will depend critically on the relative ease of transmission by vaginal and anal intercourse and on the extent to which individuals modify their sexual behaviour. If the relative transmissibility is much the same and there is no change in sexual behaviour, the total may come to be measured in millions.'[2] That use of the word millions for the UK will frighten and indeed appal many. But it comes from Sir Richard Doll, the most eminent interpreter of medical statistics and not someone given to extravagant language. In fact, of course, behaviour has changed. The homosexual community in particular are modifying their habits, wearing condoms, and are more aware of the ease of transmission of HIV through the rectum. There appears to be less chance of transmission through the vagina, though this may be related to there being less chance of trauma and exposure of the virus to the bloodstream. There are differences too in the make-up of the virus – some strains are more virulent than others.

All of this has led the most recent scientific predictions to be less alarmist. It appears that the sharply rising incidence of the last few years may now be slowing. But it has to be said that the experts have been optimistic before. The number of patients who have died from AIDS in the United Kingdom by the start of 1988 was 687, and a further 8016 people had been reported as being infected with the human immunodeficiency virus (HIV). As has been the case in the United Kingdom since the beginning of the epidemic, most of the patients with AIDS are homosexual or bi-sexual men (84%). The next largest group are haemophiliacs (6%), and only 3% of the cases were women. Yet behind those modest statistics lies the certainty of an explosive growth in AIDS over the next decade, likely to produce the biggest public health hazard this country has faced since tuberculosis in the early part of this century.

The World Health Organization has shown, from epidemiological studies in Europe, the Americas, Africa and Australia, the main ways in which HIV can be transmitted. Firstly, sexual intercourse, heterosexual or homosexual; secondly, contact with blood, blood products, or donated organs and semen. The vast majority of contacts with blood involve transfusion of unscreened blood or the use of unsterilized syringes and needles by intravenous drug abusers; in rare cases surgeons operating on a patient with HIV in the blood have been infected as a result of cutting or pricking their skin. Thirdly, mother to child – mostly before, and perhaps during or shortly after birth, called perinatal transmission.

There is no evidence to suggest that HIV can be transmitted by the respiratory or enteric routes. Casual, person-to-person contact looks as if it can only very rarely be the source of infection. Epidemiological and laboratory studies have established that of the 'body fluids', transmission seems limited to blood, semen, and vaginal and cervical secretions. Kissing has not been documented to pose a risk of HIV transmission. While totally unproven, there is some theoretical risk from vigorous 'wet' kissing, deep kissing or tongue kissing, but this should not be irresponsibly exaggerated. There is no evidence to suggest that HIV transmission involves food, water, toilets, swimming pools, sweat, tears, shared eating and drinking utensils or other items such as secondhand clothing, or telephones.

The number of countries reporting cases of AIDS has risen dramatically, from 8 in 1981 to 123 by 1987. AIDS is officially a worldwide epidemic and the size of this epidemic has been seriously underestimated. One reason for this is that cases of AIDS are only the visible signs of a much more widespread infection. For instance, AIDS symptoms may not develop for five, eight or even more years after an individual is infected with HIV. In other words, many people with AIDS today became infected five or more years ago. We do not yet know whether every person infected with HIV will develop AIDS or AIDS-related conditions. Most scientists think that about 10–30% of people infected with the virus have developed full-blown AIDS and another 20–50% have developed AIDS-related conditions. The World Health Organization estimates that 5–10 million people are now infected with HIV and most of them do not know they are infected. If past experience holds, between 500 000 and 3 million of these people will have AIDS by the early 1990s, resulting in ten to twenty times more AIDS cases in the next five years than in the last five years.

The first reported case of AIDS in the United Kingdom was in 1981. In 1987, a research worker in the Communicable Disease Surveillance Centre estimated that there would be 20 000 to 25 000 deaths from AIDS in the United Kingdom by 1992. There have been more frightening predictions but, by any standard, we are once again facing issues of public health that many people have forgotten or have never known about. Fortunately in Britain we have the NHS to cope with this epidemic and there are few other health systems in the world as well placed to meet the challenge of AIDS. Yet over the years, the public health voice of the medical profession has been considerably reduced in its influence within the decision-making structure of the NHS. To ensure that the public is fully aware of the scale of the problem that we face over AIDS we will have to develop new patterns of partnership between the practitioners of public health care and the public, far more informal and less paternalistic than in the past. A good model is what is emerging in San Francisco. The NHS will have to be able to respond quickly to changing patterns of behaviour, and to do this, the promotion of health and preventive care requires a different type of public health doctor, one readier to encourage public participation, better prepared to use the media, willing to speak a quite explicit language, and above all, willing to uphold confidentiality.

The government, after an initial hesitation, responded vigorously. In terms of a national advertising campaign, it is spending money and demonstrating concern. In view of this, it is all the more disappointing that it has not been prepared to grapple with anything like the same urgency with the immense hazard of the proven link between AIDS and drug misuse. The Advisory Council on the Misuse of Drugs in its report of that name[3] was categoric in saying that 'the spread of HIV is a greater danger to individual and public health than drug misuse' and said the situation in Scotland was a cause of 'grave concern' with 50% prevalence of HIV amongst injecting drug users. It called for a substantial increase in funding for services for drug misusers but was met with a swift government refusal to provide more funds. This rejection of the key recommendation was an act of folly. It was somewhat lost in the more newsworthy rejection of free syringes for addicts, and condoms for prisoners. It is not easy for government to appear to condone injecting drugs by supplying free syringes, though it undoubtedly should. It is even harder to accept that with prisoners sharing cells in grossly overcrowded accommodation, homosexual activity is impossible to stop. Yet both practices provide an all-important bridge for spreading HIV into the heterosexual community. To refuse to fund a major improvement in services so as to reach more drug users and educate them about the perils of AIDS is to allow prejudice over drugs policy to hazard the public's health. It is simply unforgivable and must be changed.

The reason I am so adamant is that I have experienced myself the consequences of not taking sufficient action in time. In 1970, I had been strongly influenced on blood transfusions by reading Richard Titmuss' book, *The Gift Relationship*,[4] a remarkable analysis of the defects of having a market in blood. That study showed quite clearly that where people were paid to donate blood, there was a marked tendency to lie about past illnesses, particularly episodes of jaundice. As a result, people were donating blood abroad knowing that they might have had hepatitis and this blood was coming into the United Kingdom. In 1974, when I became Minister of Health, we were very conscious of the risk of the hepatitis B virus that produces infectious hepatitis being transferred through blood products to the recipient of a blood transfusion. We had only just found ways of testing a donor's blood for this virus and there were obvious risks of other viruses being in blood products. It was also becoming ever clearer that by relying on blood products from overseas we were running a far greater risk of contamination than if we had relied purely on our own blood transfusion service. In January 1975, I was able to announce after a very difficult internal argument within the DHSS that the National Health Service would become self-sufficient within a few years for the production of Factor VIII and AHG concentrate. This would stop us being dependent on imports and make the best-known treatment more readily available to people suffering from haemophilia.

What then happened is a saga of incompetence and inefficiency which I am still trying to persuade the Health Ombudsman to investigate. The DHSS did not pursue the policy of self-sufficiency and we did not become self-sufficient in the late 1970s and instead will only become self-sufficient in the late 1980s. As a consequence, there can be little doubt that some of the people who are now HIV positive and had received blood transfusions for haemophilia and other reasons were given donor blood products from abroad which had HIV in them, when we should have been transfusing only blood products given without payment to our own regional blood transfusion service. There is a sombre lesson from this experience which we should learn for the future – prevention is not something that can be delayed without, in human terms, tragic consequences for individuals.

Though HIV has penetrated the heterosexual community in developing countries, particularly sub-Saharan Africa and South America, it is easy to forget, particularly in view of some of the TV advertising focusing on male and female sexual behaviour, that as yet HIV has hardly touched the heterosexual population in the UK. Everything possible should be done to restrict that spread. Heterosexual drug users are by far the most likely source of AIDS infection amongst women. To limit this spread of infection ought to be for the present the highest public health priority. We know the whole key to prevention is to isolate a focus of infection and to contain it. We know there is an expanding focus of AIDS in the drug community. Ten years on, unless we can change the government's mind soon, we will look back on this decision largely to ignore the advisory council's report as being a monumental error of judgement. In the United States, where a substantial number of people use drugs, the spread of HIV into the heterosexual community is proceeding apace. The number of drug users with AIDS is 13 489 – a quarter of all AIDS cases. In New York, the proportion is 33% and rapidly increasing, and while AIDS is now the major cause of death of men between 25 and 44 years of age, it is also the leading cause of death for women between 25 and 34 years of age. It was found in an unpublished study at the Bronx's Montefiore Hospital[5] that 40% of the drug users interviewed shared needles less frequently now because of the risk of contracting AIDS, but 51% said that they shared because of the unavailability of clean needles. With warning signs like this clearly flagged for all to see, the Prime Minister – as I have already warned her in the House of Commons[6] – is allowing the government to be appallingly shortsighted.

The economic cost of AIDS to the NHS is now certain to become, over the next decade, ever more formidable. The 3000 new cases of AIDS expected to be diagnosed in the UK during 1988 could result in therapeutic and care costs of more than £80 million, enough to provide, as estimated by the Office of Health Economics, acute hospital treatment for 120 000 non-AIDS patients. We are only just beginning to realize what is needed for AIDS patients. Our first AIDS hospice with nine beds opened in February 1988 at the Mildmay Mission Hospital in Hackney, East London; eight more beds are planned. The London Lighthouse in West London will open with twenty-four beds also in 1988. It is estimated that London alone needs 250 hospice beds for AIDS patients by the end of 1988.

The Mildmay Hospice occupies the top floor of a voluntary hospital supported by the Church. The ward had to be rebuilt at a cost of £610 000 of which the DHSS contributed a quarter, the rest came from voluntary contributions, and four London health authorities are being asked to contract for beds at a cost of £100 a week – expensive, but not unreasonably so when compared with the £1000 a week for a bed in an acute hospital. It has a specially trained staff who need a rare sense of dedication. We can all too easily forget how hideous AIDS can be in its terminal stages, how important is privacy and how necessary is something like an electric toilet which washes and dries a patient's bottom with warm air, an essential comfort when suffering from ulcers, herpes and diarrhoea.

What are the public health lessons from the past of relevance for the future over AIDS? In 1887, the editor of *Public Health* wrote an article, 'Shall Syphilis Become Pandemic?' after the publication of a report showing 65% of the 70 642 British troops serving in India had been treated for venereal disease. The same report showed that 28% had been hospitalized for syphilis. The only treatment at the time was mercury, until Erlich discovered Salvarsan in 1910. In 1898, it was discovered that 42 in every 1000 Royal Navy personnel suffered from primary syphilis, and 28 per 1000 from secondary syphilis. Public education changed sexual habits and the more widespread use of condoms curbed syphilis. It was finally cured with the discovery of penicillin. There are some lessons from this era for AIDS. It became clear that if people who thought they might be infected were to come forward, then they had to be encouraged to do so with the guarantee of complete confidentiality. If they feared public exposure, they would keep their symptoms or their fears secret. It became commonplace to use the Wasserman blood test for syphilis almost routinely for anyone who came in contact with any blood-testing facility. People were not specifically asked if they would agree to have a blood test for syphilis but equally, if it was done and found to be positive, the confidentiality of that information was total; no doctor would agree to the information being disclosed outside the medical profession.

Why cannot the same practical common sense be used for HIV testing? Instead of talking about compulsory testing, which we know does not work, we should follow the pattern of the past and accept automatic testing. Groups at special risk should be encouraged to have regular blood tests – particularly homosexuals and drug addicts, some doctors, particularly surgeons and exposed nurses, prostitutes and people coming from parts of the world where HIV is commonplace and who have been at risk. Doctors should take a positive lead, showing no moral judgement is involved. If anyone is found to be positive, they need careful counselling but there need be no panic. Testing has been done automatically for millions of blood donors a year in Britain since 1985. Between October and December 1985, 611 694 donations were tested for HIV and 14 were positive – all were contacted. In 1986, 2 633 862 were tested – 54 were positive and only one was not contactable. In 1987, 2 594 964 were tested – 24 were positive and 2 were not contactable. The test costs 90 pence per donation. The donor when contacted is secretly counselled. No one has yet seriously suggested that this routine should be stopped or every donor asked to sign a special consent. Why should that logic not be followed where appropriate, and HIV testing be undertaken when other blood tests are done? To argue that it should require specific written approval for a HIV test is to be seriously mistaken. What is vital is confidentiality. Why is there all this fuss over HIV testing? The answer is that some homosexuals wrongly fear that routine testing will lead to persecution of anyone found to be HIV positive.

The public mood about homosexuality is very hard to read at present. There have been a few cases of homosexuals being beaten up, many verbally abused for being linked to AIDS. The totally unnecessary back-of-the-envelope type legislation and controversy surrounding the Section 28 ban on the 'deliberate promotion' of homosexuality in the Local Government Act fed the mood of concern over HIV testing. In the present climate it is tragically true that some homosexuals will avoid going into hospital for fear that they might be HIV tested. Rather than a blanket ban on such tests, it would be better to advertise that anyone who wishes to refuse to have their blood tested can make that clear at any time. But it is absurd to allow prejudice to dictate public health practice. Public health has overcome prejudice over the centuries by being brutally frank and objective. It should not stop that common-sense practice now because of an ill-informed fear. It should instead tackle the fear by explaining the basis for testing and an individual's right to refuse a test.

Public health's pervading wisdom is that social factors – housing, heating, employment and financial circumstances – are all key ingredients in determining the health of an individual or a family. It was Sir John Simon, one of the great public health practitioners, who wrote in 1858:

> The death rates of young children are, in my opinion, among the most important studies in sanitary science. In the first place, their tender young lives, as compared with the more hardened and acclimatized lives of the adult population, furnish a very sensitive test of sanitary circumstances; so that differences of the infantile death rate are, under certain qualifications, the best proof of differences of household condition in any number of compared districts. And secondly, those places where infants are most apt to die are necessarily the places where survivors are most apt to be sickly . . .

It is probably just a statistical aberration that 1988 dawned with the realization that the infant-mortality rate in Britain had risen. This is the mortality rate under one year after a live birth, and is the most often quoted statistic indicating the health of any population. It actually went up in 1985/6 from 9.4 for every 1000 live births to 9.6. The last time the infant mortality rate went up was in 1970 and that was felt to be due to the severe influenza epidemic in late 1969 affecting mothers in the early stages of pregnancy and leading to a large number of children born with low birth weights. It may well be that the figures for 1987, when available, will show a fall, continuing the long-established downward trend. But an editorial in the *British Medical Journal* in January 1988 said that, while caution was essential in interpreting statistics, there were no grounds for complacency and that the rise was more likely to be associated with public health problems than with the distressing waiting for paediatric operations that were at that time filling the newspaper headlines.

Preliminary work has suggested that the 1986 increase occurred predominantly amongst boys and there is some possibility of a link between a rise in cot deaths and cold weather. But the information is scanty with very little social data such as whether the parents were unemployed. The *BMJ* editorial warned that we may have to ask questions about the impact on these babies' health of poor housing, low pay and unemployment. It was a timely reminder of the relevance, even today, of the public health issues that were so dominant throughout the nineteenth and early twentieth centuries. It is worth recalling a few of those epidemics.

We have been so enraptured since the 1930s by pharmaceutical advances that we have forgotten that the great epidemics of the past were controlled by the tried and tested techniques of public health. It is to the practice of public health that we must now look to grapple with the Acquired Immune Deficiency Syndrome (AIDS) epidemic. It may well be that either basic research or research supported by the pharmaceutical industry will provide us with the means to overcome the effect of the human immunodeficiency virus HIV which is the cause of AIDS, although we cannot rely on this happening.

The epidemic from cholera first reached Britain in 1831. In 1849, we experienced the most severe and widespread cholera epidemic of all. That was the same year that John Snow showed that cholera was water-borne, the carrier agents being the excretion of cholera victims. So successful were we over the next few decades in controlling cholera that during 1894/5, when 42 000 died of the disease in Russia alone, no English inhabitant succumbed to the disease. Smallpox reached epidemic proportions in 1871–3, claiming 44 079 victims despite Jenner's discovery of inoculation and a national vaccine establishment being in existence since 1808 and free vaccination by Act of Parliament since 1840. After 1906, there were only minor outbreaks of severe smallpox and these were chiefly of imported origin. One of the great achievements of the World Health Organization was totally to eradicate smallpox in 1978. Few things have ever given me more satisfaction personally than being able to find initially £1 million and then another £½ million when Minister of Health in 1975 and 1976 to ensure that that WHO programme did not stall, as then looked probable, for lack of money.

Pulmonary tuberculosis proved the most formidable of the endemic diseases, though it declined steadily in the latter part of the nineteenth and the early part of the twentieth century with better housing, sanitation, food and medical care. A cure was not discovered until 1947, with streptomycin used in combination with the sulphonamides. Typhus, typhoid, diphtheria and scarlet fever were all severe health hazards in their time.

Not surprisingly, given that history, there have been dramatic changes in recorded mortality and morbidity over the past 200 years, resulting primarily from public health measures and more recently from medical and pharmaceutical intervention. It is easy to forget how high infant-mortality rates were, even in the middle nineteenth century, and they declined in OECD countries by 90% between 1900 and the early 1980s. The largest absolute decline occurred before 1950. There have been substantial increases in life expectancy and considerable changes in the cause of death. Life expectancy at birth has increased in these countries for males from 48 years in 1900, to 57 years in 1930, to 65.5 years in 1950, and 71.5 in the early 1980s. Female life expectancy increased from 50.5 years in 1900, to 60 years in 1930, to 69.5 years in 1950, and 78.5 in the 1980s. Not surprisingly in the 1980s, until AIDS, infectious diseases were seen as a minor problem and chronic diseases had become the most prevalent cause of death in OECD countries. The developed countries have undergone what has been termed an 'epidemiologic transition' in which high infant-mortality rates caused by infectious disease have virtually been eradicated, to be replaced by deaths in the middle or later years of chronic diseases. Some estimate that 80% of all deaths, and an even higher percentage of serious disability, are now due to such illnesses, much of which is simply due to the ageing process of the body not keeping up with our new-found longevity.

It is interesting, given the different health care systems, to compare the statistics of infant death rates by sex and also life expectancy in four fairly similar countries all discussed in Chapter 5 – France, Germany, the United Kingdom and the United States – see Table 3, overleaf.

What these figures show to anyone other than a statistician is how little difference there appears to be between the western industrialized nations where public health standards are high. The main statistics vary very little regardless of what country one lives in, under what health system one is cared for, or even what percentage of GDP is devoted to health care. The odds 100

145

Table 3 (i): **Infant death rates by sex (deaths of infants per 1000 live births)**

Circa	MALES				FEMALES			
	1900	1930	1950	1980s	1900	1930	1950	1980s
France	163.3	90.2	52.1	11.2 (81)	136.5	71.6	40.2	8.2
Germany	202.3	85.4	61.8	10.6 (84)	170.5	68.4	49.1	8.9
United Kingdom	160.0	71.9	32.7	12.2 (82)	131.0	54.6	25.1	9.4
United States	135.7	65.6	33.4	12.8 (82)	112.7	52.7	25.9	10.2

Table 3 (ii): **Life expectancy at birth**

Circa	MALES				FEMALES			
	1900	1930	1950	1980s	1900	1930	1950	1980s
France	45.3	54.3	63.9	70.9 (81)	48.7	59.0	69.7	79.1
Germany	44.8	59.9	64.4	71.3 (84)	48.3	62.8	68.3	78.1
United Kingdom	48.5	58.8	66.5	71.3 (82)	52.4	62.9	71.3	77.3
United States	47.9	57.7	65.6	70.9 (82)	50.7	61.0	71.2	78.4

years ago were against surviving beyond the age of fifty-four. Today, they are in favour of surviving to seventy-seven. This has probably helped to breed a degree of fatalism about prevention and complacency over the promotion of good health. It has to be recognized however that as was shown over infant-mortality rates, we are now living at a time when minute statistical differences are felt to be important, either in highlighting a weakness in our relative capacity to cope with infectious diseases, or identifying exposure to carcinogenic agencies or other products that damage health. To the trained statistician even slight differences in the statistics between countries may eventually be traced to a difference in their health care.

The Victorian public health proponents with their interventionist legislative record would be aghast at the way we tolerate today the existence, let alone the promotion, of the proven health hazards of tobacco and alcohol. No government, Labour or Conservative, has taken any serious legislative action, apart from banning TV smoking advertisements, so as to inhibit the activity of the industry to promote their products. We have in the Medicines Act the most powerful and sophisticated machinery for reducing health risks associated with the pharmaceutical industry. Yet we will not use that or introduce similar legislation to reduce the health risks associated with tobacco products or alcohol. I have described before now how in 1975, when I was Minister of Health, the Home Affairs Cabinet Committee agreed to use the 1968 Medicine Act[7] as part of a positive strategy to curb smoking. Section 105 of the Medicine Act has a provision under which Health Ministers might by Order specify a product as subject to all the many different forms of control covered by the Medicine Act. The quickest way to proceed by this method would have been the affirmative resolution procedure which theoretically could have become law within sixty days. But using an Order has its drawbacks, for in Parliament, the Joint Select Committee on Statutory Instruments might have challenged the use of an Order, though it was proper to use the Act. The industry itself might have used the courts to oppose the Order. The easy alternative was a one-clause Bill, amending Section 105(1)b of the Medicine Act.

Unfortunately, the legislation was never brought forward

because the Labour government feared too much the effect on voters and the capacity of the tobacco industry to generate criticism, firstly on the grounds of job losses and, secondly, in specious arguments about a loss of a freedom. Industry lobbyists giving currency to nonsense scare-stories about cigarettes being available on prescription did not help the collective resolve of the government. Some newspapers, reluctant to lose revenue, were only too happy to push their vested interest. The Conservative government has been, to date, every bit as craven.

The scientific case for specifying tobacco and alcohol in the Medicine Act, whether by Order or Amendment, is overwhelming. The use of the 1968 legislation would mean establishing under Section 4 of the Act a specialist committee which would provide expert and authoritative medical and scientific advice on the health risks of tobacco. This could be accompanied by a separate specialist committee to deal with alcohol. This has the advantage for the tobacco and alcoholic drinks industries that they would be fully involved and consulted before any orders or regulations could be made. This proven procedure already operates satisfactorily for the pharmaceutical industry.

Under Section 62 of the Act, it could be made illegal to sell or import cigarettes with what was deemed to be an excessive tar, nicotine or carbon-monoxide level, or containing any other specified ingredient, provided this was always done on the advice of the Section 4 Committee. Similarly, the industry could be obliged under Part V of the Act to stop or curtail specific advertising and promotion of tobacco products. The licensing powers that exist under Part II of the Medicine Act could also be used to cover substitutes or additives.

Both industries will probably still oppose such a measure, but they are now diversifying fast into other products, realizing that they cannot go on resisting inevitable change. Perhaps they might be more receptive in 1988 than twelve years ago. The Medicine Act is a proven piece of legislation, familiar to both the medical profession and to industry. Sense dictates the advantages of using a detailed complex Act, already on the statute book, which has inbuilt safeguards balancing different but legitimate interests, and above all which would put these complex issues on a firm medical and scientific base, taking the issue to some extent out of the political arena.

The industries would have an elaborate appeals machinery. The profession would have the opportunity of developing a scientifically based strategy to reduce smoking and minimize some of the worst damage for those who continue to smoke. In a complex field, there would be the opportunity of applying a comprehensive strategy of dissuasion operating not just on price but also on promotion and on the content of cigarettes. In terms of alcohol, where excess drinking is the problem, this sophisticated approach has much to offer. In both industries condemnation is no use, nor can ever-increasing Customs and Excise duties solve the problems. In some cases the increased taxes only hasten an individual's slide into poverty and destitution.

John Stuart Mill argued in the last century, in his essay *On Liberty*, that 'society has no business, as society, to decide anything to be wrong which concerns only the individual', qualifying this with the words 'society cannot be acting wrongly in endeavouring to exclude the influence of solicitations which are not disinterested'. What in a free and democratic society should be done? We cannot continue to ignore the social evil of tobacco nor the finding that people's health is damaged by exposure to cigarettes, so-called 'passive smoking'. We ought to be horrified by our sheer negligence when facing such a well-documented health hazard. The voluntary agreements that have hitherto served as the industry's window-dressing of concern do not begin to grapple with the huge problems that exist. The framework of the Medicine Act offers the basis for a new approach. It is little short of criminal neglect that successive governments have ignored the epidemic of lung cancer overwhelmingly caused by smoking cigarettes. That epidemic which started with the increase in cigarette smoking 100 years ago has been responsible for nearly one million premature deaths in the UK in the last 50 years.

Pipe and cigar smoking were replaced by cigarettes until at the peak adults were smoking on average 9.5 cigarettes a day. This has accounted for approximately 3.5% of all deaths in men and women over the age of twenty-five in this period.[8] The reduction in smoking amongst men in the last twelve years, and the introduction of cigarettes which deliver less tar to the lungs, has had a marked effect. At all ages under eighty years, the mortality in men has begun to decrease and it has decreased by more than 50% in men under fifty years of age. Women only started to smoke after the First World War and reached a peak in 1978. This accounts for the mortality rate amongst women over fifty-five years of age still rising, and if the present trend persists, lung cancer will displace breast cancer as the most common type of fatal cancer amongst women.

A health warning on cigarette packets since 1971 has been of some value, but that and the £10 million spent by the Health Education Council from 1977–85 is nothing in comparison with an earmarked £56 million spent on tobacco press advertising in 1985 alone. With smoking responsible for 90% of all deaths from lung cancer, chronic bronchitis and obstructive airway lung disease, and 20% of deaths due to coronary artery disease, it is not surprising that the overall cost to the NHS in 1984 was £370 million. Yet still no government has had the courage to legislate and to use all the scientific facts and communication techniques to change people's habits. We could do this far more effectively than has been done over the last decade.

Excessive consumption of alcohol is another major public health hazard – at least 6000 deaths a year can be attributed to alcohol. It is a factor in 62% of serious head injuries, 66% of suicide attempts and 50% of murders. It is in the background in many cases of violence, wife battering and child abuse. Surveys show a lower consumption than indicated by sales of alcohol. There appears to have been a 5% reduction for 25% of heavy drinkers for 1978–84, but among women of all ages, alcohol consumption has increased. The vigour of successive government attempts to curb drinking and driving compare with their lassitude in dealing with the mounting problem of alcoholism at work and in the home. Nevertheless, the power of the 'don't drink and drive' campaigns has contributed to the extraordinary way in which the epidemic of road accidents has been controlled. Britain now has one of the lowest rates of road accidents in the world; even so, road accidents caused 39% of all accidental deaths at a cost of £121 million in 1985.

The report of the Royal College of Physicians on the medical consequences of alcohol abuse, published in 1987, took its title from the college's submission in 1726 to the House of Commons which used the words 'A great and growing evil'. Today about one in five of all men admitted to medical wards has a problem related to alcohol abuse. Estimates vary tremendously as to the number of alcohol-dependent people there are. In England and Wales, it is thought to be between 70 000 and 240 000, and the number of problem drinkers to be between half a million and 1.33 million. As little as four pints of beer a day can give an increased risk of illness from high blood pressure, strokes, liver disease and diseases of the nervous system. We British spend more on alcohol than we do on clothes, cars, hospitals, schools or universities. In 1981 it came to £11 000 million or 7.5% of consumer expenditure. Yet despite this spending – and more than half of that will be returned to the Chancellor of the Exchequer in excise duty and VAT on alcohol – we find that the NHS and other services to help those suffering from excess alcohol are pitiful. For some reason politicians will not act. I remember it was not easy when I was Navy Minister in 1969 to abolish the rum ration for fear of provoking a political backlash.

What then should be done about alcohol services? Most of what needs to be done has been defined by the 1978 Advisory Committee on Alcoholism, *The Pattern and Range of Services for Problem Drinkers*, known as the Kessel Report. What happens is that in the struggle for resources and against competing claims, alcoholism is all too frequently pushed to the back of the queue. Unlike tobacco, where the strategy is to persuade people to stop smoking, society is, with some justification, not ready to accept that they should give up all alcoholic drinks. The strategy for alcohol has to be different from that for tobacco products. Alcohol will continue to be manufactured long after cigarettes have ceased to be. The alcoholic drink industry has to be persuaded that it is legitimate that it should finance in large part the alcohol services. For reasons explained in Chapter 10, Paying for the NHS, there is no case for earmarking the excise duty for the NHS. But a levy on the alcoholic drinks industry to finance alcohol services, in part initially and eventually perhaps in whole, is not an unreasonable claim from society. We are always being told that the NHS should be financed more by increasing the percentage of private money. That is true, but surely the private industry that causes NHS expenditure should pay for the damage it does. Even if one does not accept this argument, by 1992 the excise duties and VAT levied on alcohol will have to be brought into line at least broadly with the other ten countries of the European Community. Ireland, like the UK, taxes alcohol much more than the rest of the Community. We cannot just cut these taxes without serious consequences for health, but we could and should cut tax while replacing the revenue lost by an equivalent levy on the industry and putting that money into alcohol services. There is no reason why it should not be a separately financed and run special health authority, contracting out services to DHAs and local authorities and voluntary organizations. An alcohol treatment authority advised by a Section 4 Committee of the Medicine Act, financed by an alcohol levy.

There is a strong case in public health terms for arguing that unemployment is an epidemic with profound consequences for health in its widest context. It is assumed by too many people in all walks of life that the unemployed are idle, feckless and will work only if made to do so. The truth is that those who are demotivated and content to be dependent are the minority, not the majority; and they have been in many cases driven to dependency by the system, not of their own volition.

In 1842, the Chadwick Commission's *Report on an Inquiry into the Sanitary Conditions of the Labouring Population of Great Britain* challenged the then current belief that disease was all the fault of the undisciplined and unclean labouring class and that all that was required was greater discipline and individual responsibility. It argued instead that disease was transmitted among the labouring classes by environmental pollution resulting from overcrowding, lack of drainage and inadequate water supply. This led to the private Act of Parliament introduced by Liverpool in 1846 for the appointment of the first medical officer of health, the Public Health Act of 1848 and, later, the great Public Health Act of 1875. Our Victorian forebears needed no convincing that poverty and poor housing were associated with ill health.

A similar authoritative report which brought together the facts and countered widespread prejudice about the work-shy was the Scarman Report on the Brixton riots in 1981. It reminded us of how deep-seated and complex are the deprivations that fuel unrest and racial suspicion. Certainly in Britain today, no public health or social policy can ignore the extent of discrimination based on race in housing and in employment. Nor can it gloss over the effect of unemployment or poverty on family life.

The family is an evolving, not a static, structure. It is a living, highly adaptive mutual support organization which is not frozen in time. The Victorian, Edwardian and modern family all owe something to each other, as will the future model family – but it will have different debts. The family has its roots in its own society. In our society, those roots still owe much to the Christian, Judaeo, Humanist tradition of altruism; a tradition where the strong help the weak, the young help the old within families.

With all the discussion of Victorian values today, it is worth remembering that the proportion wholly dependent on welfare today – nearly one in seven – is the same proportion as in Mayhew's Victorian London. Neither are the differences in sexual morality so obvious. Some 60% of women conceived out of wedlock in the nineteenth century; about the same proportion of married couples admit to pre-marital sex today. Separated families are not a phenomenon of modern times – it is the cause of separation that is different. Death created as many single-parent families in the nineteenth century as divorce does today. Family size, always thought to be much larger in Victorian times, turns out on closer examination to be not dissimilar. More children were born into families, but because of the high infant-mortality rate, and the fact that children left home well below our present school-leaving age to go to work, there was not a tremendous difference between then and now in the number of children at any one time living at home.

Nor did Victorian families look after their elderly at home more than we do. The proportion of over-sixty-five-year-olds in institutional care is no higher today than it was eighty years ago. In the middle of the nineteenth century, some 8% of households contained three or more generations while today, only 4% of households contain three generations. Of course there are vastly more elderly people living in institutions today because there are now over 9 million pensioners compared to 2.5 million of equivalent age in 1900. Modern society, because of the ever-increasing number of elderly people, faces a cost in terms of pensions and health care vastly different from that of our Victorian forebears.

It is harder to be sure about other social comparisons since the statistics are not available, but it is a pretty optimistic person who can conclude that Victorian society was less violent than ours. Alcoholism was rife, there were battered wives then as now. Neglected children were commonplace. What was different was that in Victorian times, four out of ten children died in infancy. Today, modern hygiene and medicine means not only that our infant mortality has dramatically dropped, but that children with severe handicaps now live well into their middle years, whereas even a quarter of a century ago many would have died at a young age. This too carries with it a heavy financial cost in terms of invalidity pensions and health care.

It is these two changes, with most living on into old age and the severely handicapped surviving well into middle age, that ensure our population lives far longer than in Victorian times. It is a pressure which makes it inevitable that our modern society has to have its health and welfare provision under constant reassessment.

There are over 16 million people, more than a third of all families, living in poverty or at its margins. The poorest 20% of families in Britain saw their share of total income fall from 7.1% in 1975 to 6.7% in 1985. Poor people have, by and large, become better off over the last decade or so, but they have done so less quickly than the rest of the country. Inequality of income has continued to increase. There are nearly 4 million families with children living at the present income-support level. Poverty and ill health are linked.

Death itself has a strong class bias. The babies of unskilled and semi-skilled workers are more at risk. If, for example, they had the same lower death rate as babies of professional parents, 3500 babies a year would not die. Working-class children run four times the risk of accidental death. The Registrar General, who produces the statistics on death rates, classifies social class by occupation and this explains why most of the figures refer to people of working age, for it is harder to fit a class label on the elderly, and it is no longer very relevant what occupation their parents had. When one analyses the death rates from the four most common causes of death – lung cancer, strokes, accidents and stomach ulcers – one finds that the death rate increases markedly the further down the social scale one goes.

The standardized mortality rate for all major diseases except one, malignant melanoma, shows that the chances of dying of these diseases is far less if you are a professional, a little greater if you are managerial, more so if you are clerical, even more if you are skilled manual, and even more if you are semi-skilled manual, and greatest of all if an unskilled manual worker. The one exception, malignant melanoma, is a skin cancer resulting from over-exposure to the sun, which perhaps unsurprisingly, in view of the greater likelihood for the professional, managerial and clerical classes to take holidays in the sun and expose themselves to it, is the one disease category where the chance of dying decreases the further one is down the social scale.

Such statistics were first clearly identified by Sir Douglas Black in what has become known as the Black Report, commissioned by the Labour government but smuggled out into the public domain by the Conservative government in 1980 in an attempt to bury the statistics and forget the message. These findings were, however, corroborated in an updated Black Report, a publication called *The Health Divide*. That report was stifled with allegations that the chairman of the Health Education Council was forbidding its director to hold a press conference. When the House of Commons came to examine the findings of *The Health Divide*, it found government ministers resorting to the usual defence, admittedly of all governments, that more money was being spent on the NHS than ever before. What is wrong is that we are spending more money on the NHS, but all too often in the wrong places and on the wrong priorities. Prevention is still far too low in the mind of NHS decision-makers. To reduce the class gap in health statistics – which has not even narrowed, but widened – we will have to change the thinking habits of years.

Just as doctors do not look enough at the whole person, so politicians do not study sufficiently the impact of specific policies on the whole person. What may be tolerable as a policy initiative or retrenchment as viewed from one government department may be disastrous as viewed from another, or as experienced by an individual or family.

The present much-needed emphasis on the market economy within Britain unfortunately necessitates that the acquisitive impulse within us all is pushed to the fore. That must be countered by an equally strong emphasis on the responsible society in which generosity and good neighbourliness are also pushed to the fore. That is why the NHS stands out as representing a different set of values which stress interdependence and the healthy accepting a shared responsibility for the sick.

If our political rhetoric stresses only independence, we will soon lose sight of the needs of those who are chronically sick, disabled or dependent, yet who are entitled to live in dignity.

If we talk only of individuals and their rights, we fail to promote the value of community within which responsibilities are accepted willingly in order to enlarge the rights of others.

If we talk only of distribution in terms of incentives and profits and shares, we forget the need to redistribute more fairly the prosperity of the whole nation.

Chapter 10

PAYING FOR THE NHS

... A comprehensive national health service will
ensure that for every citizen there is available
whatever medical treatment he requires, in whatever
form he requires it, domiciliary or institutional,
general, specialist or consultant, and will ensure also
the provision of dental, ophthalmic and surgical
appliances, nursing and midwifery and
rehabilitation after accidents. Whether or not
payment towards the cost of the health service is
included in the social insurance contribution, the
service itself should

(i) be organized, not by the ministry concerned
with social insurance, but by departments
responsible for the health of the people and for
positive and preventive as well as curative
measures;

(ii) be provided where needed without contribution conditions in any individual case.

Restoration of a sick person to health is a duty of the
state and the sick person, prior to any other
consideration.

The Beveridge Report, 1942[1]

The new, comprehensive national insurance scheme proposed by
Beveridge in his report on social insurance in 1942 set out to
provide comprehensive income maintenance to cope with the
contingencies in life which may prevent people from providing
for themselves by working: sickness, unemployment, retirement.

It assumed that economic policies would ensure full employment so that one of the failures of the pre-war national insurance scheme should not recur. It also assumed that there would be a national health service available to anyone who needed it, regardless of means or contributions or taxes which may have been paid. It was left open whether or not payments towards the cost of the health service should be included in the social insurance contribution. Benefits under the insurance scheme outside the years of retirement would, it assumed, be for temporary periods.

Beveridge proposed that all individuals would pay actuarially calculated flat-rate contributions to a national insurance fund which would provide flat-rate cash benefits. The fixed contribution would be payable partly by employers and partly by employees and it would be calculated according to the amount needed over a person's lifetime to fund the proposed retirement pension and the average expected incidence of sickness and unemployment. There would be a small supplement to the fund from general taxation. It was, therefore, a contractual agreement between individuals and the state which would not be subject to unilateral changes. The scheme was not, however, 'funded' in the sense that today's private occupational pension schemes provide income in the future for each individual, calculated according to the amount paid in and invested on that individual's behalf, with the level of contributions actuarially calculated to ensure that the liabilities of the fund can be met.

Beveridge's social insurance scheme was implemented in the National Insurance Act 1946. It was followed by the National Assistance Act 1948 and the National Health Service Act enacted in 1948. A small part of the revenue raised from national insurance contributions was earmarked for health. The problem with this earmarking was that even though it was only a small part that went to the NHS, initially through a specific NHS stamp, this gave the widespread impression that the stamp paid for the NHS. Right from the start the public had an unreal concept of exactly how much the NHS costs.

The bulk of the NHS funding has, in fact, from the very beginning, come from general taxation. There is now an argument that the NHS should be totally funded through compulsory national insurance contributions. It has been suggested that this could be done by transferring employees' national insurance contributions from the National Insurance Fund to an earmarked health fund. To consider this proposition objectively, it is necessary first to consider the evolution of national insurance since the war and recall the considerable party political controversy surrounding the structure of national insurance.

The practical flaws in the 'comprehensive' national insurance scheme were evident from the beginning. The problems were: demands on the scheme outstripped at an increasing rate the amount raised from contributions; the numbers not qualifying for national insurance benefits were much larger than envisaged, so the safety net national assistance means-tested benefit was large and also growing; national insurance benefit rates were too low to tackle poverty, so many had to have national assistance as well; the number of pensioners increased and pensioners lived longer. The effect of all this was that the fund which paid for contributory benefits became dependent on the upper limit figure of an 18% Treasury supplement to meet obligations to pensioners. It is only recently that that percentage Treasury supplement has been reduced, to 5% of the total fund in 1988/9. It is probable that this government's intention is eventually to withdraw all Treasury supplement.

These pressures contributed to the resistance by successive governments to raising benefit levels under the national insurance scheme because of the enormous cost involved. The basic state retirement pension was relied on by millions to be adequate for a comfortable old age, but it became barely adequate and, for many, it was never high enough to cover their inescapable housing costs. Even though benefit levels were relatively low, demands on the fund led to higher contribution levels and income tax than foreseen. This pointed up the flaw in the principle of the scheme – because contributions were levied at a flat rate, the higher they rose the more the burden increased on the low paid because the relatively low paid had to spend a higher proportion of their earnings on their contributions than the better off.

A growing body of opinion in the late 1950s began to argue

that contributions should be earnings-related, like income tax, but the belief that benefit entitlement should be individually based and directly related to contributions, which Beveridge had articulated, was still held strongly by many in all political parties. It was argued, therefore, even within the Labour Party, that if contributions became earnings-related, benefits must be too.

Successive governments changed the rules of the national insurance scheme to limit its cost, with benefit entitlements and levels frequently changed to the detriment of those who had paid contributions. The gap between the benefit demands on the scheme and contributions made to it accelerated in the first decade until major changes had to be made in the late 1950s. The government abandoned the actuarial link between contribution levels and benefit demands. The Exchequer contribution was capped at an arbitrary proportion of the then current income of the National Insurance Fund, and contributions were increased sufficiently to cover the cost of benefits, net of the Exchequer contribution. Graduated contributions related to income were first introduced in 1961 and contributions became earnings-related, as a percentage of income, in 1975. They were payable on *all* income once a threshold of income was reached, unlike income tax, so the relative burden still fell most heavily on the lowest paid. Because contributions were graduated, a graduated pension scheme was promised too, but abolished on the introduction of the State Earnings Related Pension Scheme (SERPS), with benefit entitlements preserved.

In part because the old age pension never provided an adequate income for retirement on its own, there was a rapid expansion of occupational pension schemes during the 1950s. Employers and employees contributed an actuarially determined percentage of annual earnings to funds which would pay benefits according to formulae linked to the amount of contributions paid in and the number of years for which contributions had been made. By the mid-1960s, about half the working population – about 11 million people – were contributing to schemes and this proportion has remained stable since. In 1969, Richard Crossman legislated for a national superannuation scheme. The election intervened and Edward Heath's government was not prepared to implement it, and instead replaced it with legislation which gave the dominant role in extending pensions to the private sector while establishing a government-run and funded scheme deliberately inferior to all but the poorest private pension schemes. Again, an election intervened and this scheme was not implemented by the incoming Labour government in 1974.

It was to the credit of Barbara Castle as Secretary of State for Social Services and Sir Geoffrey Howe as Conservative opposition spokesman that they both recognized that this appalling legislative record, coupled with the wafer-thin Labour majority in 1974 and 1975, made compromise inevitable. The Labour government sought an accommodation with the Conservative opposition. A major effort was made to secure a permanent reform of pensions across party lines which would be acceptable to the various pensions interest groups. It was generally agreed that pension reform was long overdue and that stability for the next few decades was essential. This was achieved in the establishment of the State Earnings Related Pension Scheme which went through Parliament without significant opposition on its underlying principles.

It is worth recalling how SERPS has been able to survive in the midst of party political controversy through a little judicious compromise, since it gives some pointers as to how we might find a basis for a cross-party agreement over the funding of the NHS. When the SERPS legislation went through Parliament, the Conservatives promised not to alter it. Because SERPS is not a funded scheme – except to the extent that guaranteed minimum pensions are funded in the private sector – it is relatively easy to alter. Even if it were funded, because each Parliament is sovereign and cannot bind its successors, it could always be changed.

The Conservative government, re-elected in 1983, initiated a major review of social security in 1984. The Secretary of State for Social Services said that this review was not intended to call into question the 1975 cross-party settlement. Yet in the Green Paper published in 1985,[2] the government proposed to end SERPS and to make all employers and employees contribute to funded private occupational or personal pension schemes. SERPS would continue only for those within fifteen years of retirement. The justification most rehearsed by the government was that SERPS was unaffordable – it represented, so it was argued, a gesture by today's politicians which placed a very high and unreasonable burden on tomorrows' taxpayers. This was not generally accepted to be the case by disinterested experts and, in the Green Paper, the government accepted that modifications to the future cost could be made while retaining the scheme, though it itself rejected that option.

It was clear that there was no possibility of the Labour Party ever agreeing to the Conservative government's proposals to end SERPS. Abolition would have meant far inferior pension arrangements for the low paid and people working only intermittently than, for all its inadequacies, would have been the case with SERPS. For these millions of workers, compulsory private schemes would be exceptionally expensive to administer – a cost which employees and employers would have to meet – with expensive transferability arrangements. Furthermore, pension levels would depend on the number of years of contributions made while SERPS offered a full pension based on twenty years.

Although SERPS was by no means generous to low-paid workers it would be, at least, more generous than the Conservatives' privatized alternative. SERPS was cheap to administer and had no transferability problems. So customers would get more for their money. Increasing the basic state pension while abolishing SERPS, as the Liberal Party wanted, would have meant immediate increases in taxation on employees and their employers contracted-out of SERPs, and had the support of no other political party.

The pension industry was haunted by the fear of returning to the previous situation where there was no cross-party agreement. The SDP was appalled at the prospect of renewed political instability. So began the search to clarify some agreement on the principles which had formed the basis of the agreement over SERPS in the 1970s: the desirability that that half of the working population which did not benefit from occupational schemes should be able to contribute to higher pensions for their retirement; a scheme which would fit the employment patterns of people taking on domestic responsibility and with intermittent employment; and a state scheme because the private sector could not meet these objectives. The Conservatives in the 1970s had acccepted this and they saw then that occupational-scheme growth had halted naturally in the early 1960s. A modified SERPS would reduce the expense to future generations and reform of the structure could give relatively more help to the lower paid. The pensions industry and employers were dismayed by the government's proposal to end SERPS and they forcefully argued that the private sector through compulsory insurance could not provide adequate pensions for those at the bottom end of, or only sporadically in, the labour market.

The government eventually was persuaded to abandon ideology in favour of common sense and agreed to retain but restructure SERPS. The SERPS restructuring led to the level of guaranteed minimum pension, in occupational schemes eligible for contracting out, being reduced from 25% to 20%. The contracted-out rebate has been recalculated to reflect the lower guaranteed minimum pension required of occupational schemes. In 1988/9, employers' national insurance contribution is 5% of the salary of employees earning between £41 and £69.99, 7% for earnings between £70 and £104.99, 9% for earnings between £105.00 and £154.99, and 10.45% for all employees earning over £155.00. The contracted-out rebate – 35.8% in total from 1988/9 to 1992/3 divided between 3.8% on employers' contributions and 2% on employees'.[3] Employees' national insurance contributions are: £49 to £69.99 a week – 5% on all income; those earning between £70 and £104.99 a week – 7% on all income; and £105 to £305 a week – 9% on all income; above £305 a week, 9% on income up to £305. So no national insurance contributions are paid on weekly earnings above £305.

Against this history of ideological polarization on pensions, familiar in other policy fields as well, many are rightly very suspicious of making any changes in the existing method of financing the NHS. A test of any new method for funding the NHS is: Is it likely to last? That means there must be some measure of cross-party agreement.

If the Conservative government, Labour opposition and the SDP could agree on pensions in 1986, surely it is imperative that, if there are to be any major changes in the funding of the NHS and before legislation is rushed through, an attempt is made to forge agreement on at least the principles underlying such legislation? We must try to avoid going through again the experience over pensions, with the financing of the NHS becoming a similar political battlefield. It would be better to continue with the status quo of funding the NHS through the Exchequer grant out of general taxation than for any new scheme to be kicked around by the political parties like a political football.

The choice before the country is: do we go on limping along, spending broadly 6% of GDP on health care, tilting the balance between private and public spending so that the private sector contributes more than at present, or as a country, are we ready to pay for a step-like increase in spending on health care of the order of 1–1.5% of GDP? Only if that decision is envisaged is it worth contemplating major structural reform of the funding of the NHS.

It has to be admitted that the current method of financing the NHS has many practical advantages – the administrative costs appear, despite difficulties in making fair comparisons, much lower than those in countries with insurance-based systems. Admittedly, with decentralized cost-accounting being extended in the NHS, administrative costs will be likely to rise, but that is a reasonable price to pay if efficiency improves as it should do. In countries with private insurance systems, doctors are paid on a fee for each item of service. The evidence is that in these systems not only are costs very hard to control – much harder than in the NHS – there is also unnecessary treatment. In the mid-1970s, for example, three times as many hysterectomies were carried out per 100 000 population in the US compared with England and Wales and nearly four times as many cholecystectomies.[4] Financial controls in the NHS, by contrast, minimize unnecessary treatment.

The NHS has, however, been unable to maintain an efficient level of capital spending; even more than revenue, the capital account has been held down. The last review of the age-structure of NHS buildings in England conducted in 1981 showed 7% were built before 1890, and 74% between 1891 and 1918. Between 1919 and 1939, 5% were built; 6% between 1940 and 1964 and 8% from 1964 to 1981. This capital neglect carries with it high maintenance-to-capital ratios which eat into revenue. The problem with new capital building, however, is that in most cases the revenue consequences of capital spending are even greater. So capital investment, though increasing over the last five years, has a long back-log to make up.

In part, this capital neglect is the inevitable consequence of the current method of financing the NHS, which varies from month to month, let alone year to year. It highlights the inappropriateness of Treasury controls for a government department when applied to such a complex area of management as the NHS. This was a problem I first encountered as Minister for the Navy when trying to run more efficiently the then four royal dockyards. As Minister of Health, it was even worse, and I longed for the managerial freedom of having an independent budget where we could plan ahead for four to five years, sure that the investment would be there and not subject to pettifogging Treasury controls that stipulated how much we could transfer between the capital and revenue account. The Treasury operates on a short-term cycle wholly inappropriate for the NHS.

Restructuring the NHS to build in competition between providers and to offer choice to consumers, introducing mechanisms such as an internal market, building on social security payments so as to develop a form of vouchers to offer choice to poorer long-stay patients so they can purchase the form of care that suits them, encouraging the movement towards health maintenance attitudes are all worthwhile mechanisms for improving the quality of care without another disruptive reorganization. They can be done without changing the fundamental principle that care is provided on the basis of need and not on the capacity to pay. But none of these changes is likely to produce a quantum jump in better standards in the NHS, better health care, nor remove feelings of frustration and dissatisfaction that are felt, not just by health care professionals when they are not able to match those demands because of limited finance, but also by the general public. Such a quantum jump in standards can come only from a deliberate decision to increase the proportion of GDP that we spend on health.

One of the ironies of the present debate about reform of the

NHS is that it has exposed the one undoubted success of the NHS in comparison to other countries' health systems, namely its capacity to contain health care costs. If maintaining health spending at around 6% of GDP continues to be the highest priority for a British government reviewing the NHS, then whatever its political persuasion, no government will wish to change from the present Exchequer grant system. Yet the public is now demanding of its politicians a system of health care of a far higher standard than we are currently providing through the NHS. The question is, should government respond and provide such a higher standard? To do so, the NHS will need more money and better management. This could be done within the present Exchequer grant system, but it is politically far more likely to be done within a new financial structure. Managerially, there are also considerable gains to be made from a new financial structure if the NHS is put on to an independently funded basis.

Some have argued that the NHS should be financed in part by taking all the money raised in taxing tobacco and alcohol, as these are health related. There are a number of objections to such a proposition, the most important being that it is in the interests of the health of the nation that the fall in smoking cigarettes and in alcohol consumption should be so great that the revenue from taxes on them would fall as well. It would be wrong for the NHS to have a vested interest in maintaining a high tax income to the extent that the rate of tax should never be so high as to so discourage consumption that the return from tax actually fell. It is better, as suggested in Chapter 9 on public health, to raise a levy from the alcoholic drink industry to pay for alcohol-related Health Service provision.

A health fund in the main would have to come from either a hypothecated tax or from compulsory health insurance contributions. By introducing a health fund, we would deal with one of the major problems that has detracted from the efficient running of the NHS since 1948, namely the incapacity of the Treasury to let those who manage the NHS have any financial stability in the medium term, let alone the long term. The NHS has never been able to plan forward sensibly. It frequently does not know how much it has to spend until its financial year is well under way, and it not infrequently has its financial arrangements changed under it during the financial year. A separate health fund must provide a 'ring fence' from the annual public expenditure cycle to which other government revenues are subject. Such a ring fence, once established by either contribution or hypothecation, could allow, with other complementary changes such as an internal market, the NHS to operate far more efficiently. It would also allow the NHS to borrow in the market. It would be possible to create a bond market in Britain such as operates in the United States where public utilities and cities have access to this source of investment independent of federal or state finance.

Another advantage of a hypothecated or contribution-based health fund would be its transparency – people could see how much they were paying for the NHS. If people wanted better health, government could respond but people would immediately feel in their pocket what such demands were costing them. Both a contribution-based and a hypothecated tax would provide a buoyant source of money, contributions being linked to the movement of wages in the economy, a health tax being linked to movement in incomes more generally.

The crucial question to answer, however, over any alternative method of financing, is would it better facilitate the achievement of a step-like increase in health spending over a 4–5 year period from just around 6% to 7–7.5% of GDP; in 1988/9 money terms, an increase of £3–£5.5 billion. Also, would the method chosen ensure that the extra money provided actually delivers higher standards of care?

The principles behind any new scheme for financing the NHS cannot ignore the past history of NHS funding or social security funding. It should aim to ensure that:

1 The cost of health care is not higher for sick or high-risk groups.
2 The well off should contribute to the cost of health care more than the less well off.
3 High standards should be available equally when medically needed for all.
4 Better treatment, or faster treatment, should not be related to the capacity to pay.

The NHS can be developed in ways in which patients have considerably greater consumer choice, and there are a multiplicity of providers without flouting any of these principles. Yet in the NHS we have at present, there has been an erosion of these very principles. Higher standards are not available equally, many are buying privately faster and even better treatments. Waiting lists are, in some parts of the country, a disincentive to stay within the NHS.

The NHS is presently financed to the extent of nearly 82% of the total out of *general government revenue*. This does not just include income tax, but also value added tax, betting taxes, excise duties, capital taxes and corporation taxes. Expenditure is allocated out of this general revenue to all government spending departments including health and personal social services expenditure under the DHSS. Thus the NHS is not just financed out of income tax, but from the whole gamut of revenue-raising tools. In addition, as has been emphasized earlier, there is, as there has always been, a contribution from national insurance contributions. In 1987/8, this contribution was £2.73 billion, 13% of the cost of the NHS or 7% of the total resources generated by national insurance. In addition, the NHS raises money directly in charges. In 1987/8, this raised £1.1 billion or 5.5% of the total NHS budget. Income from pay-beds will probably increase with better marketing from its current level of around £60 million, but the charges made are already broadly comparable to those within the private sector.

The recent increase in dental, ophthalmic and prescription charges has meant and will increasingly mean that some sick and high-risk groups have found the price too high to pay. In 1979, prescription charges were 20p an item. In 1988, they went up to £2.60 an item. People either fail to attend for treatment or, even allowing for 60% exemption, some still fail to present the prescription to the chemist. The scope for much more money for the NHS from this charge is not great. The present charges can probably continue to rise with inflation, without any further adverse effect, but to increase them over and above inflation again would have very bad consequences.

The decision by this Conservative government in 1988 to legislate for the first time to charge for dental check-ups and sight-testing breached the very important principle that there should be no financial bar in the way of early diagnosis. It is to be hoped that Conservative MPs who rebelled against this will give short shrift to the suggestion that patients should be charged for visiting their GP. The principle of free access is worth upholding and charging for dental check-ups and sight checks should be stopped by any different government. The arguments of the profession are not mere vested interest – blindness can be prevented if glaucoma is picked up early, teeth can be saved if dental caries is identified early, lives can be saved if oral cancer is detected early. It is a foolish government that overrides genuine professional advice in an area like this.

The only new area of charging that deserves examination is 'hotel' charges for inpatients in hospital. This does have a quantifiable economic advantage in providing a discipline to concentrate everyone's mind on keeping an inpatient stay for diagnosis and treatment to the minimum. When examined in the past, hotel charges have been rejected as much because of their high cost of administration as for any principled objection. I first suggested looking at such charges in 1968[5] and examined it more carefully when Minister of Health in 1975. The problems associated with hotel charges were discussed though rejected by the royal commission in 1979. On their assumptions of 60% exemption and a 10% reduction in the length of stay, a nominal charge of £10 per day would yield up to £150 million – although administrative costs might reduce that sum by as much as a half.[6]

It is not worth considering introducing this on its own for acute patients. It would be wiser to consider it in the context of reviewing the entire board-and-lodging payment system for acute and long-stay patients in hospitals and homes relating to social security payments. The present situation contains many anomalies. The well-off elderly person suffering, for example, from a mild case of Alzheimer's disease affecting the brain and particularly the memory, at present pays the full cost if they are in a local authority old persons' home or a private psycho-geriatric home, but pays nothing if they are in a psycho-geriatric bed in an NHS hospital. A similar person without any personal financial resources is paid through income support money to cover their board-and-lodging costs when in a local authority or private home, but the NHS is unable to recover their costs against an income support claim when they are in hospital. Yet social security not unreasonably makes a reduction in pensions after a six-week period away from home. Whether such patients go to hospital or a local authority or private home with nursing care often bears little relationship to their medical or mental state but reflects rightly either personal choice or the availability of accommodation. The whole system is an illogical mess.

The issue of personal choice is one of the important questions which is raised by the current review of community care and is dealt with in Chapter 8. There is a strong case for the social security and tax system being integrated, thereby operating cost-effectively and fairly. If a care voucher for everyone in need of long-term care was introduced, the NHS ought to be able to recover their costs from social security. This would be a transfer of money, but it would be a useful addition to health budgets and would need to be taken into account in assessing any new formula for funding the NHS. It would be another suggested private source of money like health bonds and an alcohol levy.

At present, it is the mix of finance which ensures that the NHS is funded from a wide base. It is a reasonable simplification that in principle around 13.2% of all revenue raised goes to the NHS. A contribution-based health fund would significantly diminish the number of people contributing to the NHS. Only 18 million people pay national insurance contributions, so if they were to bear the whole cost of the NHS it would represent an average cost to each contributor of £1200. If the cost of the NHS were spread across those paying income tax through a hypothecated health tax, the average cost would be £980, whereas the average cost of the NHS spread over all those over the age of eighteen would be around £535. The average cost across the whole population, or the per capita health spending, is around £365 up to £400 if one includes private spending. When analysing how this is made up, it has to be remembered that an acute hospital bed costs £100 a day and a single case involving complicated surgery, like a baby with a hole in the heart, can cost £10 000, thereby absorbing the annual allocation for twenty-five people.

Some argue that spreading the cost evenly across the

population would mean everyone would be aware of how much health costs. Some even want everyone to have a voucher which they could use to cover all their own risks for acute and chronic illness through insurance. Either way, that would be a flat-rate poll tax for health and would be deeply regressive and, as the controversy over the poll tax has shown, bitterly resented. The unpopular prospect in April 1990 of the local government poll tax, called the community charge, means that whatever the arguments for a flat-rate health charge giving the same signal to all individuals about the cost of the NHS, it is hard to see even Mrs Thatcher being ready to have two such charges operating simultaneously.

Loading the burden of the NHS on to a reformed national insurance base undoubtedly could meet its funding requirements, but then the revenue would come only from the working population of employees and employers. Also, with the upper earnings limit to national insurance contributions, this would transfer the weight of NHS funding from higher incomes to those on low incomes. An advantage is that funding the NHS totally through a compulsory insurance-based contributory system, in accountancy terms, would give a more independent funding system than by hypothecating income tax. Total funding by contributions was, however, something that Beveridge considered but implicitly rejected when he left open 'whether or not payment *towards* the cost of the health service is included in the social insurance contribution'. What is perhaps surprising is that, despite modifications over the years, we still maintain some of the original concepts behind the Beveridge 'contributionary principle' within national insurance contributions: the upper earnings limit, the exclusion of pensioners and the retention of the national insurance fund as the source of financing for those benefits which depend on a contribution record.

Successive governments have altered the real value of benefits, introduced earnings-related supplements to benefits and abolished them, changed the up-rating formulae and steadily increased the level of contributions. The Conservative government, primarily to finance the growing cost of unemployment benefit, put national insurance contributions up for most employees from 6.25% in 1979 to 9%, earnings-related unemployment benefit has been abolished, unemployment benefit has been made taxable, and in the 1986 Social Security Act, maternity and widows' national insurance benefits entitlements were reduced. National insurance contribution is a clear payroll tax on employers – a situation confirmed in 1985 when the government abolished the upper earnings limit for employers' contributions in the budget that year to increase revenue. The effect of the tax is also to be a 'tax on jobs'. Although the Conservatives removed Labour's national insurance surcharge, when unemployment is still high and Britain's unit costs are still high by comparison with our key competitors, there are serious disadvantages in putting added burdens on the employers' contribution to national insurance contributions. Indeed, there is a strong case for a regional reduction in employers' contributions to cut the cost of employing someone and create more job opportunities.

As a comprehensive income-maintenance scheme, Beveridge's social insurance scheme has failed. In 1987/8 only 54% of all social security income transfer expenditure came from contributory benefits. Of this, nearly 75% was attributable to the basic state pension[7] and neither the state pension nor unemployment benefit, which is now the other major national insurance benefit, is sufficient of itself to relieve poverty. The total income from national insurance in 1988/9 is expected to be £30.3 billion, estimated to be £15.9 billion from employers and £14.4 billion from employees.[8] It is the second highest revenue raiser for government after income tax. The cost of the National Health Service in 1988/9 is estimated to be £23.5 billion.

The former Home Secretary, Leon Brittan, has argued that national insurance employee contributions should be simply transformed into a national health fund, the present national insurance contributions would be abolished for employees and they would pay national health insurance contributions set at a level to meet precisely, with NHS charges, the cost of the NHS.[9] Such a scheme would, however, merely mean a transfer of the savings to the Exchequer grant from having the NHS funded through contributions to the insurance fund so as to make up for employees' contributions. This would substantially increase the existing topping up of the national insurance fund by Exchequer grant. The effect of the scheme would be to have two funds: the existing national insurance fund paid for in part out of insurance, and far more than before out of tax; also a new national health insurance fund paid for substantially out of employees' insurance contributions and NHS charges.

This simple idea, for what would be effectively compulsory health insurance financing all health expenditure, has, when carefully examined, formidable problems. These relate to the balance of taxation and the change in philosophy of reducing the contribution element in the funding of important social security benefits. The philosophical problem with taking employees' national insurance contributions to finance the NHS is that the national insurance fund would move away from only 5% at present coming from a Treasury supplement to even more than the present 18% limit on money coming direct from the Treasury. Restructuring of national insurance by introducing a substantially larger element of Exchequer grant would be an even greater departure from the Beveridge principle than hitherto. It would be odd for a Conservative government to do it. It would be totally against the recent trend of their policy whereby they have been moving to a fully contribution-based benefit structure for the insurance fund.

At present, £25 billion of benefits are drawn exclusively from the national insurance fund, and while some of the principles for the foundation of such a system have been breached over the years, there remains a direct and immediate relationship between national insurance contributions and those national insurance benefits. It would be hard to justify scrapping the entire notion of contribution-based benefits merely as a consequence of a desire to change the basis of NHS funding.

The Conservative proponents of an insurance-based method of funding also do not give sufficient weight to the structural changes within the existing system that would be required to make it politically acceptable as the major source of NHS funding. Many of these changes are themselves complex, and costly. They are valuable ends in themselves, though not easily achievable, particularly not in the wake of the wasted opportunity of the 1988 budget. National insurance rates, which occur in three bands (5%, 7% and 9%), are not, like income tax, payable on the *next* pound of income, but on *all* income. This is highly regressive, and one of the causes of the current disincentive trap.[10]

To take a simple example: if a person's income rises from £40.50 per week to £42.00 per week, crossing the £41 national insurance threshold, they start to pay national insurance at a rate of 5%, not just on that first pound earned above the threshold, but on their *entire* income. In this case it would mean the individual's income rising by £1.50 per week and incurring £2.10 tax through NICs, so ending worse off as a result of a pay rise. This phenomenon also occurs when income crosses the respective thresholds for the higher national insurance rates of 7% (£70 per week) and then 9% (£105 per week). It hits precisely those on lowest incomes, traps them and dampens their incentive for working harder, or working overtime, in order to increase their income. In this respect the existing national insurance contribution structure is both iniquitous and inefficient.

National insurance contributions also, unlike income tax, have an arbitrary 'ceiling' of £305 per week, beyond which no national insurance is paid at all on any extra earnings. This means, for example, that someone earning £110 per week – 50% of average earnings – pays 9% NICs on *all* their earnings, but a person earning £660 per week – 300% of average earnings – pays national insurance only on the first £305. So someone with a marginal tax burden of 34% (25% income tax and 9% NICs) experiences a fall in the burden to 25% if their income reaches £305 per week and this does not rise until earnings reach £370 per week, at which point 40% income tax is payable, *but still no marginal national insurance*. The person on half average earnings actually pays a higher average rate of NICs than the person earning three times the average income. There is absolutely no justification for such an arbitrary, inefficient and incoherent system and to continue with that system as the main source of finance for the NHS would discredit the new financial framework from its inception.

To integrate the tax and benefits systems effectively, the bottom threshold for national insurance contributions must be brought into line with the single person's tax allowance. This means, in effect, raising the lowest threshold for NICs from £41 per week to £50 per week, so that nobody pays NICs without

174

also paying income tax. National insurance would then be altered so that its impact is as a marginal rate on earnings above the threshold. This would involve making the first £50 per week exempt from NICs and scrapping the 5% and 7% NIC rates. A single 9% rate of NICs operated on a progressive scale and compatible with income tax would reduce the tax burden of all who pay NICs on their whole income, including those currently paying the 5% NIC rate. Because there are so many people concentrated at the bottom end of the income scale, this reform of NICs would, however, cost more than £2 billion. To introduce it would mean removing 800 000 poor people from tax altogether. It would transform once and for all the NICs structure into a fair and progressive part of the tax system.

To remove the financing of the NHS from general taxation and to put it through the existing national insurance contributions structure would be regressive, though this would be minimized if employees' national insurance contributions were made into a progressive tax which followed the rules of income tax. Abolition of the £305 limit would, however, amount to a 9% increase in effective marginal tax rates for all those earning £15 860. Such people are by no means rich, particularly not where families depend on a single income. The rational way to have dealt with this problem would have been simultaneously to remove the NIC ceiling and reduce quite substantially all rates of tax at the same time. This is what the Chancellor of the Exchequer should have done in the 1988 budget. Not only did he fail to do so when cutting the top marginal rate of income tax to 40%; but by leaving in place the NICs ceiling he made it virtually impossible ever to achieve this fundamental reform of NICs without offsetting that 9%. It is now clear that this Conservative government is not likely to make employees' national insurance contributions progressive, nor is it giving a high priority to tidying up the anomalous and unfair national insurance contributions structure.

Another political objection to insurance funding for the NHS is that it will open the door to a two-tier health service. It is claimed, though it is a claim open to considerable challenge, that a compulsory insurance scheme would retain the 'sacrosanct' principle behind the NHS that 'adequate health care should be available to everybody in the land, irrespective of their means'. Yet a major reason for many Conservatives advocating this change in national insurance appears to be that it would facilitate 'opting out' by those choosing to take out private insurance. If a contribution-based national health insurance fund were to be introduced, Conservatives will argue there should be a rebate available to those who contribute to private health insurance schemes. On the Conservative side, it would be pressed strongly because most of those who argue for a national health insurance fund do so because they want opting-out along the lines of the existing SERPS.

In seeking a cross-party agreement on funding the NHS, we need to be very clear about the principles which are worth preserving. If one could opt out from any health fund, the effect would be alarming. Those most likely to opt out would be the better-off and low-risk groups who expect to make few demands on the NHS. The financial burden for all the high-risk groups – the elderly, chronically sick, AIDS sufferers – would then fall on those who choose to stay fully in the NHS, or have to do so because of low incomes. This is the experience of West Germany – hardly a health care system to copy – where people on higher incomes can opt out of the compulsory social insurance which is calculated as a percentage of earnings (6.3% of employees' salary, matched by employers). Opt-outs are taken up by affluent and low-risk people because the private schemes, by excluding high-risk and chronic sick cases, can charge lower premiums. The burden of financing the expensive cases therefore falls on the less well off.

Some concede that if there is to be any opting-out, it would have to be partial, a limited SERPS-like opt-out, confined to non-urgent referrals to hospital mainly for elective surgery. That might be not as damaging, but a vital principle would have been breached – that we all take out an insurance policy by contributing to the NHS and we never know when we will benefit. The rich person's luck can run out and they can no longer pay their insurance cover. We can all be victims of a long and expensive illness. Also, we all use the accident and emergency services.

If a Conservative government thinks it is politically desirable to give an incentive to increase private health insurance, then that can be achieved more simply and with less potentially damaging effects through adjusting tax allowances to encourage private health insurance. To propose contribution-based funding just to introduce a SERPS-like opting-out mechanism is a bad rationale for a scheme that has many other flaws.

A further objection to funding the NHS from national insurance contributions is that NIC excludes pensioners. Besides putting the load on to the working population, it would damage one of the four basic principles already identified: that funding of health care should redistribute from the well to the sick. At present, we all, if reasonably well off, whether twenty year olds or eighty year olds, take our share of paying for the sick, including the millions of mentally ill and mentally handicapped. To exclude the elderly from paying a contribution to benefits has an inner logic given the history of the social security system that has grown up over the years. But there is no logic in stopping the old from paying through income tax towards the funding of the NHS.

For all these reasons, creating a national insurance fund by juggling around and transferring the NIC employees' contribution to health, and transferring the Exchequer supplement for health to the insurance fund to pay social security benefits, is not the best option.

A better system, if the political will exists, would be to introduce a hypothecated health tax. A new health fund could be designed to take its revenues from this earmarked part of income tax. The individual's tax return would have a separate line for a health tax in addition to income tax. A health fund would have to be able to be financed unless changed by legislation for a four-to-five-year period. It is highly desirable if the NHS is to operate as an efficient organization for such a fund to be designed to last. It would need to be based on a specific formula tied to the growth of GDP, health criteria and buttressed by independent assessment by the government actuary. Since its revenue base would still be built up from charges as well as income tax, there would be an element of income which the NHS would itself control. The NHS would also control receipts from land and building sales which the National Audit has shown can be a source of greater revenue. The present national insurance contributions to health would be forgone by the NHS and could pay for a much-needed tidying up of the structure of national insurance contributions.

A formula which could help in the design of a health fund has come from the Institute of Health Services Management in a report published in 1987. Health spending, it is suggested, should rise with national income augmented with provision for demographic changes like the elderly, new service requirements such as AIDS and any major pay restructuring. The problem with such a formula is that if it started at the present low base, all the existing difficulties would continue. Health expenditure in the past has vacillated considerably, rising in fits and starts depending on circumstances, sometimes even going up more than the rise in GDP. This has been because the financial base had never been secure and has varied with public-expenditure reviews and IMF-imposed constraints.

The Royal Commission on the NHS, when it considered hypothecation, felt that 'no government is likely to relinquish control over NHS expenditure however it is financed. Hypothecation by itself would therefore neither increase spending on the Health Service nor remove it from political control.' That conclusion underestimates the extent to which public opinion is now forcing government to face up to the need to restart health spending from a much higher base. It also does not reflect the extent to which government thinking has moved towards being ready to hive off some of the activities of central government departments. There is no longer a strong political belief that the NHS is best run by a government department and by civil servants. Rather to the contrary, there is a much greater openness about the merits of separating the NHS from day-to-day politics and having a national health authority. There is also a greater readiness to accept the need to find a mechanism to confront the electorate with the financial consequences of meeting every desirable health demand. This means the old arguments about hypothecation are not held with the same conviction.

Provided there can be a legislative basis for the formula similar to that which exists for the national insurance fund and that a health fund is also overseen by the government actuary, there is no reason for anyone in or outside government to fear the consequences of such a change. The government must be free to change the formula to provide more or less funds at statutory intervals, normally of four to five years. They would, if following representations from the health authorities that the fund was insufficient, be under pressure to be more generous. Or if the public felt they were paying sufficiently for a given standard of health care, the government might increase funds for the NHS on a less generous basis. The key would be to increase financial stability but retain a degree of periodic political flexibility.

The Treasury has always objected in principle to hypothecation. Experience with the road tax fund, which was meant to finance roads then ended up making more money and contributing to general tax revenues, is often quoted. Also, if a health tax, so the argument goes – why not an education tax? Why not a defence tax? A political argument for a specific health tax is that health, of all government services, involves everyone as individuals in a personal way from the cradle to the grave. In that sense, health service provision is like social security provision which is already earmarked. But the real political argument for bucking the convention and having a specific health tax is that this is the best way of letting the public know what health care costs and making them feel a responsibility for its provision. At a time when health costs are bound to continue rising, the demand for health care needs to be clearly linked to the cost of paying for health care.

Health trends can now be forecast with a fair degree of accuracy for four to five years ahead, so fixing the formula for a fund would not be impossible. There could be an addition to the formula, ensuring that if the buoyancy of income tax was exceptionally insufficient to cover normal inflation, then as a minimum the fund would be inflation-proofed out of the contingency fund for that year. This would give the NHS a two-way insurance that is no more than a reflection of present-day practice. Above all, a health fund, if the political will is present, would give the NHS stability in its financial management which is needed if it is to get the best value for patients out of money spent, whether in hospitals or in the community.

The attraction of a health tax is that it might gain cross-party agreement. The different parties could tilt the balance of tax allowances to encourage or discourage private insurance as they ideologically wish, without affecting the structure. There would have to be in return an agreement not to allow anyone to opt out of the health tax or pay at different rates. To do this would destroy any chance of all-party agreement. It would also have even less justification than opting out of a contribution-based system. No one opts out of paying for state education.

An advantage of taxing health separately is that it increases the Chancellor's room for manoeuvre. It is not impossible that a future government in a budget might decide to cut income tax yet increase the health tax. That is a perfectly rational decision. Another government might choose to raise both taxes. A right-of-centre government might well adjust tax allowances to deliberately encourage greater private health insurance provision. A left-of-centre government might adjust them to discourage private health insurance. What would then be happening is the exercising of a perfectly legitimate political choice but operating such a choice in a stable structure. There would be an underlying acceptance, as happened over SERPS, that the fundamental structure of health tax would remain unchallenged. This sort of all-party understanding is worth compromising to achieve. A prerequisite is that there will be a step-like increase so that we devote 7–7.5% of GDP to health. There is little point in making the change to a health tax unless it is marked by a decision to spend more on health.

To achieve such a step-like increase from 5.9% to 7–7.5% of GDP spent on health would require, as stated previously, an increase in expenditure on the NHS from around £22.38 billion (gross cost excluding revenue from charges) to between £26 billion (7% of GDP) and £28.5 billion (7.5% of GDP). If the 1988/9 cost of the NHS was raised by hypothecating in a health tax the necessary proportion of tax revenue in addition to the revenue from charges, there would be, instead of the 25% income tax rate, a health tax in the region of 14% and income tax of 11%. If the proportion of GDP spent on health was raised to 7%, the proportion of health tax would increase to around 16%, with 9% income tax. If 7.5% of GDP was committed to the

NHS, health tax would need to be in the region of 17%, with 8% income tax. This excludes private money from health bonds, an alcohol levy, or board-and-lodging refunds. If the basic rate of income tax was cut to 20% the remaining income tax element over and above health tax would then be so small one could scrap basic-rate income tax altogether, raising the revenue forgone from other parts of the tax base, perhaps from changes in expenditure taxes like VAT. This would mean that basic-rate taxpayers would pay only the health tax, while those paying the current 40% top rate of tax would pay both health tax and 40% top rate income tax.

A very welcome effect of such a health tax is that it would make the current contribution to the NHS from NICs unnecessary. This revenue, running at just under £3 billion in 1988/9, should be utilized to increase the national insurance threshold. This would resolve a major anomaly in the national insurance structure already described and make NICs progressive and compatible with the income/health tax structure.

If these changes were coupled with moves to bring together the tax system and the benefits system into a compatible tax/benefits structure, it would be possible at the same time to address the question of the poll tax. The integration of the tax and benefits systems, which will be entirely feasible once the Inland Revenue and DHSS are fully computerized, would eliminate the vast majority of instances where government gives benefits with one hand and takes back taxes with the other. With an integrated tax and NIC threshold it would be possible to bring poll tax into line, ensuring that nobody below the threshold would pay any tax, national insurance or poll tax. Poll tax would be included in the tax/benefits calculation as part of overall tax burden and benefit entitlements. The extra tax burden would be calculated on a progressive scale. This would transform the poll tax into a local income tax, a genuinely fair system of funding local government. It would bring very closely into line the health/income tax, national insurance and poll tax structures.

The whole system would then be reasonably simple and demonstrably fair. It would provide a system of funding for the NHS which would give it the necessary autonomy, flexibility and managerial efficiency, and also facilitate the step-up in the base of funding which the political, social and economic climate of Britain now needs and demands.

As a doctor and as a politician, I have never wavered in my wholehearted commitment to a National Health Service which provides care on the basis of medical need, which delivers care quickly, considerately and efficiently, and which is able to grow to meet new demands which are constantly placed upon it. There is no case for dismantling the fundamentals of our NHS, nor for making changes in the method of funding which undermine those principles. The establishment of a separate health fund for the NHS, funded principally from an earmarked health tax, addresses the need for change without introducing anything like a two-tier health service. It could provide the basis for a political compromise ensuring both the flexibility which changes of government require and the assured and stable financial foundation the NHS must have if it is to retain public confidence. To revive our NHS, we as taxpayers must value it by being prepared to pay for it.

References

I Our NHS

General references
Rudolf Klein. *The Politics of the National Health Service*, Longman, 1983

Ruth Levitt & Andrew Wall. *The Reorganized National Health Service*, Croom Helm, 3rd edition, 1984

Health Care Provision Under Financial Constraint, edited by T.B. Binns & M. Firth. Royal Society of Medicine Services, 1988

Health Economics, edited by George Teeling Smith. Croom Helm, 1987

The Health Service in England Annual Report 1986–87. HMSO

David Owen. *In Sickness and in Health: the politics of medicine*, Quartet Books, 1976

II The Medical Profession

1 Anonymous. 'American versus European medical science', *Medical Records* 4, 1869, pp 133–4

2 Starr, P. *'The Social Transformation of American Medicine: the rise of a sovereign profession and the making of a vast industry'*. Basic Books, New York, 1982

3 Neutra, R. 'Indications for the surgical treatment of suspected acute appendicitis: a cost-effective approach', essay in *Costs, Risks and Benefits of Surgery*, edited by Bunker, J.P., Barnes, B.A., Mosteller, F. Oxford University Press, New York, 1977, pp. 277–307

4 Vayda, E. 'A comparison of surgical roles in Canada, and England and Wales', *New England Journal of Medicine* 289, 1973, pp. 1224–9

5 Owen, David, 'Medicine, Morality and the Market', The Osler Lecture, Montreal, April 1984

6 Review Body on Doctors' and Dentists' Remuneration, Eighteenth Report, 1988, Cmnd 358

7 Buck, N., Devlin, H.B., Lunn, J.V. *Report of Confidential Enquiry*

into Peri-operative Deaths, Nuffield Provincial Hospitals Trust, December 1987

8 Steel, K., Gertman, P.M., Crescenzi, C., Anderson, J. 'Iatrogenic illness on a general medical service at a university hospital', *New England Journal of Medicine* 304, 1981, pp. 638–42

III The Nursing Profession

1 Roper, N. Logan, W.W., Tierney, A.J. *The Elements of Nursing*, second edition, Churchill Livingstone, 1985

2 Tony Delamothe. 'Nursing Grievances', *British Medical Journal*, Volume 296, six articles, 2 January–6 February 1988

3 Second Report of the House of Commons Social Services Select Committee 1984/85, *Community Care*, Volume 1, HMSO, 1985

4 'Neighbourhood Nursing – a focus for care', *DHSS Report of the Community Nursing Review*, HMSO, 1986

IV The Creation, Structure and Evolution of the NHS

1 Abel-Smith, B. *The First Thirty Years*, HMSO

2 Powell, J. Enoch. *Medicine and Politics: 1975 and After*, Pitman Medical, 1976, p. 14

3 Owen, D., Spain, B., Weaver, N. *A Unified Health Service*, Pergamon Press, 1968

4 Royal Commission on the National Health Service, chaired by Sir Alec Merrison. Cmnd 7615, July 1979

5 Second Report of the House of Commons Social Services Select Committee 1984/85, *Community Care*, Volume 1, p. xlviii, HMSO, 1985

V Lessons from Abroad

1 Lalonde, M. *A New Perspective on the Health of Canadians*. Government of Canada, Ottawa, 1974

2 Iglehart, John. 'Canada's health care system', *New England Journal of Medicine*, September 1986

3 Graham Turner, 'NHS: Quest for a cure', *Daily Mail, March 1988*

4 *German Health Service Under Review*, information sheet issued by the government of the Federal Republic of Germany, January 1988

VI   A Market in Health

1 Castle, B. *The Castle Diaries 1974–76*, Weidenfeld & Nicolson, 1980

2 Enthoven, Professor A. *Health Plan*, Addison–Wesley, 1980

3 Enthoven, Professor A. *Reflections on the Management of the NHS*, Nuffield Provincial Hospitals Trust, 1984

4 Goldsmith, M. and Willetts, D. *Managed Health Care: a new system for a better health service*, Centre for Policy Studies, February 1988

VII   Waiting Lists

1 Yates, J. *Why Are We Waiting?*, OUP, 1987

VIII   Community Care

1 *Second Report of the House of Commons Social Services Select Committee 1984/85, Community Care.* Volume 1, HMSO, 1985

2 *Community Care – Agenda for Action.* Report to the Secretary of State for Social Services prepared by a Committee under Sir Roy Griffiths, February 1988

3 Wagner Committee. *Residential Care, a Positive Choice*, HMSO, March 1988

4 Report of working party on residential accommodation. *Public Support for Residential Care*, DHSS, July 1987

IX   Public Health

1 Director of Nursing, Mildmay Aids Hospice, quoted in *New Society*, 19 February 1988

2 'Major epidemics of the twentieth century, from coronary thrombosis to AIDS', Sir Richard Doll, *Journal of the Royal Statistical Society*, Series A, Volume 150, Part 4

3 Report by the Advisory Council on the Misuse of Drugs. *AIDS and Drug Misuse*, HMSO, 1988

4 Titmuss, R. *The Gift Relationship: From Human Blood to Social Policy*, Allen & Unwin, 1971

5 'The Lessons of AIDS', *New Society*, 8.4.88

6 Hansard, col. 31, 31 March 1988, HMSO

7 Owen, David. '*A Future That Will Work*', Viking Press, 1984, pp. 142–4

8 *Social Trends* 18, HMSO, 1988

X Paying for the NHS

1 *The Beveridge Report*, Social Insurance and Allied Services, HMSO, November 1942

2 Reform of Social Security, Volume 1, Cmnd 9517, June 1985

3 Chancellor of the Exchequer's autumn statement, House of Commons paper 110, November 1987

4 Owen, David. 'Medicine, Morality and the Market', The Osler lecture, Montreal, April 1984

5 'Social services for all', Fabian Society Essays, 1968

6 *'Health Finance: Assessing the Options'*, Kings Fund Institute, 1988

7 *White Paper on Public Expenditure.* HMSO, January 1988

8 *Financial Statement and Budget report.* HMSO, March 1988

9 'A new deal for health care'. Leon Brittan QC MP, Conservative Political Centre, 1988

10 'Fair Tax, Fair Benefits', SDP, March 1988

Index

Index

A

Abortions 96
  Act of 1967 96
administrative districts 55
Advisory Committee on
    Alcoholism 151
Advisory Committee on Misuse of
    Drugs 138
AIDS epidemic 135–42, 144, 145,
    176
alcohol 147, 148, 149, 150–51
  excise duty on 149, 151–2, 166
Alcoholics Anonymous 28
Alzheimer's disease 28, 169
amenity beds 94
  see also pay-beds
American Medical Association 22,
    107
ancillary workers' strikes 110
area health authorities 54, 55, 56
area health boards 54
Association of Anaesthetists 24–5

B

Bath Health Authority 133
Belloc, Hilaire, quoted 92
Bevan, Aneurin 47, 49, 72, 94–5,
    97, 101
  quoted 44
Beveridge, Sir William (late Lord)
    160, 171, 172

Report 157
  Welfare State model 85
Birmingham hospital services 46
Black, Sir Douglas 155
blood donation 138–9, 142
blood transfusions 136, 139
British Medical Association 58, 99
  against market and competition
    51
  and consultants' contracts 100
  and health service finance 45
  opposition to state control 16,
    22, 48, 49, 54, 98
  and pay-beds 98, 99
  representation of profession 36
Brookestone, Mrs 98–9
Brown, Ernest 46

C

Califano, Joseph 102
Canada 79–83
  health care in 5, 81–2
  'extra billing' in 82
  hospitals in 80
  item-by-service payment 18, 80
  universal insurance system in 80,
    82
Canadian Medical Association 82
carer's charter 7, 132
Castle, Barbara 55, 72, 97,
    98–100, 161
Castle Diaries 1974–6, The (Castle)

98-9
Central Committee for Hospital
  Medical Services 111
Central Council for Nursing,
  Midwifery and Health Visitors
  40
Chadwick Commission report 152
Charing Cross Hospital 98
cholera epidemics 144
Churchill, Winston 47
clinical freedom 15, 16, 20–21,
  29, 105
clinical team concept 23, 31–2, 57
community health care 17, 28, 59,
  72, 90, 119–34
  carer's allowances 127, 128–30,
    132
  elderly and 119–20, 122–7
  House of Commons report on
    67
  individual choice in 124–5, 130,
    132, 170
  meals-on-wheels 133–4
  mentally ill/handicapped and
    119, 120, 121, 123
community health councils 9, 12,
  55, 66, 115
community nursing 41, 42
Community Nursing Review
  report 42
consultants
  contracts 58, 98, 99–100
  salary structure and merit
    awards for 49, 95–6
  and waiting lists 115
  work to rule by 110
consultation/treatment statistics 8
consumer choice 125, 127, 168,
  170
  rights, satisfaction 10–11, 109
Cripps, Sir Stafford 94
Crossman, Richard 54, 72, 160

D

Dawson Report (1920) on Medical
  and Allied Services 45
de Gaulle, Charles 85
demographic factors 34, 40, 122
dental practitioners 50–51
  payment and working practice
    51, 67
dental services 49–51, 53
  charges 50, 168, 169
  free check-up 49–50
Department of Health and Social
  Services 139, 141
  assessment of 72–3
  and community care 126, 130,
    133
  involvement in NHS 60, 65, 68
Disablement Income Group 129
district health authority 4, 43, 56,
  57, 58, 60, 63–6, 67, 68, 101,
  102, 103–5, 115
  and health maintenance
    methods 108
  and internal market 7, 65, 68,
    102, 103–6, 107
  proposed linkage with FPC
    58–9, 108
  relationship with RHA 64–6
  role of 11, 12
  and waiting lists 115, 116–18
district nurses 42
Doll, Sir Richard 135
Doncaster Health Authority 114
drug abuse, syringes and AIDS
  136, 138, 140
Duthrie, Sir Robert 114

E

East Anglia Regional Health
  Authority 105

elderly, care of 11, 52, 84–5, 115, 176
  community care and 119–20, 122–3, 131, 133–4
  private homes for 96, 101, 126, 127
  in residential care 123, 125, 126, 127, 131, 153–4
Emergency Medical Service (1939) 46
Enthoven, Professor Alan 102–3
epidemics 144–5
executive councils 48, 53, 54

F

Family Practitioner Committee 43, 55, 57, 67, 68
  budgetary control of 58
  proposed linkage with DHA 58–9, 67, 68, 105, 108
fee-for-service payment 75, 76, 77
  see also item-by-service payment
France 85–7
  customer orientation in 87
  health care expenditure in 5, 86–7
  hospitals in 85–6, 87
  infant mortality/life expectancy in 145–6
  Sécurité Sociale 85
Freeman, John 95

G

Gaitskell, Hugh 94
general management philosophy 11, 12, 23
General Medical Council 17, 19
general practitioners 49, 53, 91, 97
  administrative vehicle for 55
  clinical freedom of 105
  contractor status 47, 67, 94, 107
  group practices and 107
  health maintenance organizations and 108
  independence of 49, 51, 54, 57
  new role and influence 27, 69
  patient relationship 11, 13–14, 15, 29
  pay structure 54, 91
  and preventive medicine 59, 69
  separation of GP and hospital services 51–2, 54, 57
geriatrics 8–9
  hospitals for 115
  see also elderly, care of
Germany 87–91
  Allgemeine Ortskrankenkasse 88, 89
  health care expenditure in 5, 89
  hospitals in 89
  infant mortality/life expectancy 145–6
  insurance systems 88–90, 176
  over-supply in 87, 89
  sickness insurance in 16
Gift Relationship, The (Titmuss) 138
Goodman, Lord 100
Grabham, Mr, surgeon 100
Griffiths, Sir Roy 57, 122, 124–5, 130
  First Report (NHS management) 11, 41, 57, 132
  Second Report (community care) 41, 122, 124–5, 126, 127–8, 131, 132, 133
Guillebaud Report 53

H

Haemophilia 139
Harris, Mr, orthopaedic surgeon
 112
Health Advisory Service 42, 115
health bonds proposal 6–7, 167
health care economics 7, 17–21,
 93
health care expenditure 5–7, 58,
 172
  capital spending 164–5
  cash limits 58
  financial autonomy 60, 68, 82
  prescriptions, cost of 58
  as proportion of GDP 5, 6, 17,
   53, 61, 91, 164, 165–6, 167,
   177, 180
health centres 47, 54, 107
Health Commissioner
 (Ombudsman) 9, 139
Health Divide, The 155
Health Education Council 150,
 155
health inspectorates 115, 128
health maintenance 7, 59, 69,
 105, 165
  health maintenance
   organizations 22, 75, 77–8, 79,
   106–8
  see also preventive medicine
health promotion officers 57
health service administration
  Acts relating to 52, 55, 158
  tripartite structure of service 48,
   52–4
  see also area health authority,
   district health authority,
   regional health authority
health service financing 6–7, 45,
 46, 157–9, 163–82
  Exchequer grant 160, 166, 172,

 173
  from general taxation 158, 164,
   168, 170
  insurance contributions 158–9,
   163, 166, 168, 171–5
  proposed health fund 166–7,
   170, 173, 177–8, 179, 182
  proposed health tax 7, 166, 170,
   177–82 *passim*
health visitors 42, 52
Heath, Edward 57, 160
hepatitis B 139
HIV *see* AIDS
holistic approach to health 25–6,
 27, 29–30, 32
hospice movement 28
hospice nursing 42
Hospitals Consultants Staff
 Association 36
Hospital for Sick Children, Great
 Ormond Street 2, 60
hospital/family practitioner
 linkage 7
hospital management committees
 54
'hotel' charges 169
Howe, Sir Geoffrey 161
Hutchison, Sir Robert, quoted 13
hypothecated health tax 7, 166,
 170, 177–82 *passim*

I

Iatrogenic disease 24–5
In Place of Fear (Bevan) 44
Independent Hospitals
 Association 34
Independent Pay Review Boards
  Doctors' 35
  Nurses' 35–6, 37
infant mortality 8, 23, 143, 145–6,

153, 154
Institute of Health Services
  Management report 178
internal market philosophy 19,
  64–5, 68, 91, 102–5, 167
  inter-DHA market 7, 65, 68,
    102, 103–6, 116
  public/private mix to NHS 92–5,
    101
item-by-service payment 18, 51,
  54, 75, 76, 77, 107, 164

J

Japan 71, 83–5
  health care expenditure in 5, 83,
    84
  insurance schemes 83–5
Jenner, Edward 144
Joint Consultants Committee 93
joint funding, for community
  care 120–22
Joseph, Sir Keith 41, 55, 57

K

Kessel Report, on alcoholism 151
Kings Fund 6

L

Lalonde, Marc 80, 81
Lancet, quoted 1
life expectancy 145–7, 154
Lloyd George, David 44
local authority 48, 53, 55
  community care and 120–22,
    127–8, 130, 131, 132
  role of 11–12, 46, 47

London County Council hospital
  services 46, 48
London Lighthouse 140

M

Malpractice insurance 76, 77, 79,
  103
management structure 41, 48,
  52–4, 56, 57
  clinical management teams 23,
    31–2, 57
marketing orientation, in health
  care 22, 23, 27, 29, 103, 107
Maternal Deaths, Confidential
  Enquiry into 23
Maude, Sir John 53
Medical and Scientific Laboratory
  Organization 37
medical audit 7, 19, 23, 105
medical priorities 1, 20, 59
medical profession 13–30, 91
  clinical freedom of 15, 16, 20–21
  confidentiality 15
  independence of 15, 16, 54
  NHS contracts 94
  patient relationship 11, 13–14,
    15, 25
  and preventive medicine 138
  professional representation of
    36
  women in 43
medical research 69–70
Medical Research Council 69
medical schools 17–18, 28
Medicines Act 147, 148, 149, 152
mentally ill/handicapped 11–12
  community care and 119, 120,
    121, 123
  hospitals for 115
  private homes for 96

services for 11–12, 42, 52
merit awards, for consultants 23,
    49, 95–6
Merseyside Health Authority 114
Middlesex hospital services 46
midwives 52
Mildmay Mission Hospital,
    Hackney 140–41
Mill, John Stuart 149
MIND 121
Morrison, Herbert 48
mortality rates 145–7, 150, 154–5
  see also infant mortality

N

National assistance 158, 159
National Association of Local
    Government Officers 47
National Development Team for
    the Mentally Handicapped 115
national health authority
    proposal 178
National Health Service
  Acts relating to 52, 55, 158
  Management Board 23, 59, 68,
    93, 104, 105, 106
  tripartite structure of 48, 52–4
national insurance 44–5, 46, 47
  Beveridge proposal 157–8
  contributions to 159–60, 163,
    170, 171–5, 181
  introduction of 16, 44
  NHS and 158–60, 163, 168,
    171–5
National Insurance Fund 159,
    160, 172–3, 176, 177
New Perspective in the Health of
    Canadians, A (Lalonde) 80, 81
Nightingale, Florence, quoted 31,
    33, 36

Northern Ireland, health
    organization in 59, 67
nurse practitioner 42, 43
nursing profession 31–43
  accommodation and transport
    39–40
  dissatisfaction in 34–41
  education and training 40
  no strike commitment 36, 37
  in private sector 34
  'patients first' attitude 32
  pay awards to 35, 52, 56
  RCN-union representation 36–7
  recruitment 33
  role of 31–3, 41, 42–3
  shortages in 8, 33–5
  staffing levels 37–8
  see also community nursing,
    practice nurse

O

On Liberty (Mill) 149
Osman, Samira 76
Owen, Dr David 1–2, 53, 55, 61,
    76, 97–8, 100, 102, 144
Oxford Health Authority 144

P

Patents 70–71
patients' rights 9–10
  see also consumer choice
patients' travel costs 117–18
pay-beds 56, 87, 94, 97–8, 99,
    100–101, 168
pay review structure 35–6, 37
pharmaceutical industry 69,
    70–71, 144, 147, 148
physician/patient relationship 11,

13–14, 15, 25, 29
Politics of Defence, The (Owen) 102
poll tax 171, 181
Poor Law services 45, 48
Pope, Alexander, quoted 13
Porritt, Sir Arthur 53
post-surgery deaths 24
poverty, and community care 154
Powell, Enoch 52
practice nurse 42
preferred provider organizations 106
prescription charges 86, 90, 94–5, 168
Prevention and Health: Everyone's Business (Owen) 81
preventive medicine 7, 25–7, 29, 52, 59, 77, 81, 90, 107, 108, 138, 155
primary health care 42, 59
Princess Grace Hospital 113
Priorities in Medical Research (House of Lords report) 69
private health insurance 19, 21, 45, 74, 91, 101, 106, 113, 176, 177
  fee-for-service system 75, 76, 107, 164
  in United States 16, 74, 75, 78, 79, 106
private nursing agencies 38
private sector medicine 93–4, 95, 96–8, 101, 113
  no. of beds/hospitals in 101
professions allied to medicine 52
Project 2000 40–41
psychiatric care 42, 121
  private nursing homes 101
  see also mentally ill/handicapped
public health 135–56
  AIDS/HIV, impact of 135–42, 144, 145

alcohol and tobacco risks 147–52
  epidemics 144–5
  mortality rates 145–7, 150, 154–5
Public Health Acts, 1848 and 1875 152
Public Health magazine 141

R

Regional health authority 43, 55, 58, 60–61, 64–5, 68, 105
  role of 60, 63–4, 66, 104
  suggestions for improvement 66
regional hospital boards 48, 54
resource management 7, 60–63, 93, 104, 106
  experimental initiative in 93
  Resource Allocation Working Party formula 61–3, 64, 104, 116
  service increment for teaching 63
retirement pensions 158, 159, 160–63
Review Bodies 96
  on Doctors' and Dentists' Remuneration 23, 52
Robinson, Kenneth 53, 54, 97
Rothschild, Lord 69
Royal College of Nursing 32, 36–7
Royal College of Physicians 150
Royal Commissions
  on Local Government 54
  on Medical Education 53
  on National Health Insurance 45
  on National Health Service 56, 100, 178
Royal Marsden Hospital 60

S

St Bartholomew's Hospital 113
St Mary's Hospital, Paddington 112
Scarman Report 152
schizophrenia 28, 70, 123
Scotland 138
  health organization in 59, 67
Seebohm Committee 53
Shaw, G. B. quoted 3, 10, 21
Sheffield Health Authority 114
Simon, Sir John 143
smallpox 144
Snow, John 144
social insurance 74, 157, 158
social security, and community care 124–31 *passim*
Social Services Select Committee 121
Socialist Medical Association 46
Society of Medical Officers of Health 47
South East Thames Health Authority 114
South Tees Health Authority 111
South Western Region Health Authority 114
Surrey hospital services 46

T

Teaching hospitals 60, 61, 63, 64
Tebbit, Norman 112
Thatcher, Margaret 57, 106, 127, 132, 140, 171
Titmuss, Richard 138
tobacco, health risks of 147–50
  excise tax on 166
trade unions 52, 97, 99, 101
  COHSE 35, 36, 99
  NUPE 35, 36, 98, 99
tuberculosis 144
Turner, Graham 88

U

Unemployment, community care and 152–3
United States 70, 75–9
  corporate medicine in 22, 25
  health care expenditure in 5, 6, 23, 26, 75, 77, 103
  HMOs in 22, 75, 77–8, 79, 106–7
  iatrogenic disease in 24–5
  infant mortality/life expectancy 145–6
  malpractice insurance in 76, 77, 79, 103
  marketing philosophy in health care 22, 25, 103
  medical profession in 14–15, 16, 21–2
  Medicare, Medicaid 16, 22, 75–8 *passim*
  nursing profession in 43
  preferred provider organizations 106
  preventive health care 25–6, 77
  private insurance sector 16, 75, 78, 79, 106
  spread of AIDS in 140

V

Venereal disease 141
voluntary hospitals 45, 46, 47, 48
voucher system 7, 127, 131, 165, 170, 171

W

Wagner Committee 125
waiting lists 4, 7, 37, 87, 101–2,
    109–18, 168
  initiatives to reduce 111,
    114–15, 116–17
Wales, health organization in 59,
    67
ward closures 4, 33
Well Women clinics 28
Wessex Regional Health
    Authority 34
West Berkshire Health Authority
    114
West Midlands Health Authority
    114
Whitley Council 35
Willink, Sir Henry 47
Wilson, Harold 56, 95
Woolton, Lord 47
World Health Organization 136,
    137, 144

Y

Yates, John 115
York University Social Policy
    Research Unit 125
Yorkshire Health Authority
    114

Kenneth Harris
David Owen Personally Speaking to Kenneth Harris
£4.99

From boyhood to the present day, David Owen talks frankly of his private and public life, his plans, hopes and beliefs.

Beginning with his Welsh childhood, through his time at university and in the medical profession, to a career in the Labour Party and the subsequent formation of the Social Democratic Party, David Owen discusses his life in revealing detail.

He relates his experiences in a number of government posts – Navy Minister, Health Minister and, particularly, Foreign Secretary 1977–9 – and provides unique insights into the Falklands, Anglo-American relations, Africa and the Middle East, Iran, defence and disarmament, and the European Community. He also discusses candidly his relations with many prominent politicians, including Jimmy Carter, Leonid Brezhnev, Menachem Begin, Harold Wilson, James Callaghan and the other three members of the 'Gang of Four' who founded the SDP.

His reasons for leaving the Labour Party in 1981 and the birth of the SDP are covered in detail, and David Owen tells why, with his belief that social democracy has a special contribution to make to British politics, he is continuing as leader of the SDP.

Stuart Bell MP
When Salem Came to the Boro £3.99
the true story of the Cleveland child abuse crisis

It was the greatest child abuse crisis that Britain has ever faced. At the heart lay the fundamental question: who has ultimate power over children – the family or the state?

In 1987, a total of 197 Cleveland children were taken into care during a six-week period on allegations of sexual abuse.

The removal of their children had tragic consequences for many of the families involved, and led to an escalating conflict between the state, social services and those responsible for diagnosis.

The resultant national outcry focused world attention on Middlesbrough (known locally as 'the Boro') and a crisis which would bear comparison with the Salem witch hunts of the seventeenth century.

In *When Salem Came to the Boro* Stuart Bell, Labour MP for Middlesbrough, reveals the chilling truth behind the horrifying events of May and June, 1987.

Pauline Cutting
Children of the Siege £3.50

'We will stay with the people of the camp until the danger is over. We will remain with them – to live or die with them'
Children of the Siege is Pauline Cutting's moving account of life and death in the Palestinian camp of Bourj al Barajneh, Beirut.

It is an impassioned record of a heroic struggle to save lives in near impossible conditions of bombardment, starvation, malnutrition and dwindling medical resources – a struggle which is still going on.

Above all, it is the story of courage and comradeship shown by the doctors and nurses who have come to the camps from all over the world, and the people they are trying to save.

Dr Cutting spent eighteen months in Beirut, working day and night in make-shift operating theatres and helping the wounded – many of them children – while bombs exploded around her and snipers lay in wait outside. *Children of the Siege* is her true story, an unforgettable testament of the fight to save lives in the face of death.

John Pilger
Heroes £4.99

'Pilger is the closest we now have to the great correspondents of the 1930s . . . The truth in his hands is a weapon, to be picked up and brandished and used in the struggle against evil and injustice' GUARDIAN

'Pilger's *magnum opus*: a passionate and utterly absorbing collection of reports from the firing lines, both abroad (Vietnam, Cambodia, South Africa) and home (the East End, the miners' strike, Fleet Street) by one of the dwindling bunch of journalists in this country with heart as well as a hard nose' TIME OUT

'A tough, responsible book . . . Pilger's strength is his gift for finding the image, the instant, that reveals all: he is a photographer using words instead of a camera' SALMAN RUSHDIE, OBSERVER

'Some remarkable reporting is reprinted here . . . It contains some memorable snapshots of a harsh world' TIMES LITERARY SUPPLEMENT

'He is a true model for his peers and followers. Let them study for instance the awesome opening pages of the long chapter, 'Year Zero', which unforgettably describes the hideous and desolate remains of murdered Phnom Penh . . . mark, shudder, reflect and profit. There are other passages just as fine' SPECTATOR

'If I were a modern history teacher, I'd start the year's course by slinging copies of it across the desk and telling them to get on with it'
DUNCAN CAMPBELL, CITY LIMITS

All Pan books are available at your local bookshop or newsagent, or can be ordered direct from the publisher. Indicate the number of copies required and fill in the form below.

Send to: **CS Department, Pan Books Ltd., P.O. Box 40, Basingstoke, Hants. RG21 2YT.**

or phone: 0256 469551 (Ansaphone), quoting title, author and Credit Card number.

Please enclose a remittance* to the value of the cover price plus: 60p for the first book plus 30p per copy for each additional book ordered to a maximum charge of £2.40 to cover postage and packing.

*Payment may be made in sterling by UK personal cheque, postal order, sterling draft or international money order, made payable to Pan Books Ltd.

Alternatively by Barclaycard/Access:

Card No. | | | | | | | | | | | | | | | | | | |

Signature:

Applicable only in the UK and Republic of Ireland.

While every effort is made to keep prices low, it is sometimes necessary to increase prices at short notice. Pan Books reserve the right to show on covers and charge new retail prices which may differ from those advertised in the text or elsewhere.

NAME AND ADDRESS IN BLOCK LETTERS PLEASE:

....

Name————————————————————————————

Address————————————————————————————

—————————————————————————————————

—————————————————————————————————

—————————————————————————————————

3/87